D0903055

Richard Brautigan

The TOKYO-MONTANA EXPRESS

DELACORTE PRESS/SEYMOUR LAWRENCE

Published by
Delacorte Press/Seymour Lawrence
1 Dag Hammarskjold Plaza
New York, N.Y. 10017

Portions of this work first appeared in *Mademoiselle, Esquire, Outside,
California Living, Earth, Evergreen, Triquarterly, New Ingenue, The
CoEvolution Quarterly, New Orleans Review, San Francisco Stories,* and *The
Overland Journey of Joseph Francl* published by William P. Wreden.

A limited edition of *The Tokyo-Montana Express* was published
in different form by Targ Editions.

The author thanks them and *Playboy* (Japanese edition) for publishing his work.

Manufactured in the United States of America

First printing

LIBRARY OF CONGRESS CATALOGING IN PUBLICATION DATA

Brautigan, Richard.
The Tokyo-Montana express.

I.   Title.
PS3503.R2736T64   813'.54   80-17171
ISBN 0-440-08770-8

FOR RICHARD AND NANCY HODGE

Though the Tokyo–Montana Express moves at a great speed, there are many stops along the way. This book is those brief stations: some confident, others still searching for their identities.

The "I" in this book is the voice of the stations along the tracks of the Tokyo–Montana Express.

THE ROUTE OF THE TOKYO—MONTANA EXPRESS:

[ix]

[x]

The Overland Journey of
Joseph Francl and the
Eternal Sleep of His Wife Antonia
in Crete, Nebraska

PART 1: OFTEN, CLOAKED LIKE TRICK OR TREATERS IN
THE CASUAL

*On the third day out from Lucky Ford River we found a
corpse almost eaten by wolves (which are very numerous
here, howl in concert at night and keep us awake) and
scalped by the Indians . . . We buried him and went on
our way, with sorrowful thoughts. —Joseph Francl*

Often, cloaked like trick or treaters in the casual
disguises of philosophical gossip, we wonder about the ultimate meaning of a man's life, and today I'm thinking

about Joseph Francl: a man who brought his future to America, God only knows why, from Czechoslovakia in 1851, and completely used up that future to lie dead, facedown in the snow, not unhappy in early December 1875, and then to be buried at Fort Klamath, Oregon, in a grave that was lost forever.

I've read the surviving sections of a diary that he kept on a long unsuccessful gold mining expedition that he took in 1854 from Wisconsin to California, and some letters that he wrote back from California.

His diary is written in a mirror-like prose that is simultaneously innocent and sophisticated and reflects a sense of gentle humor and irony. He saw this land in his own way.

I think it was an unusual life that led him inevitably, like an awkward comet, to his diary and then later to his death in America.

In the beginning Joseph Francl was the son of a man who owned a brewery and a glassworks in Czechoslovakia, so he was probably surrounded by a stable world of abundance.

He became a classical musician who studied music at the Prague Conservatory and travelled with an orchestra that gave concerts in Czechoslovakia, Austria, and Germany.

I keep asking myself a question that can't be answered: Why did Joseph Francl come to America in the first place and leave so different a life behind him? There is just something inside of me that cannot understand why he came here.

Gee, it's such a long way from giving a concert, perhaps Beethoven or Schubert, in Berlin or Vienna to Joseph Francl describing the American West: . . . *after supper, we received a visit from a real wild Indian, a chief of the Omaha tribe. He said he was looking for his squaw. He had not seen her for two days, she was wandering around among the emigrants.*

That is quite distant from a concert audience waiting for the music to begin.

Joseph Francl left his own Czechoslovakian-born, American-courted wife Antonia whom he called Tony and his young son Fred behind in Wisconsin when he went out to California to find gold.

I've thought about him leaving Antonia behind. I've thought about her waiting. She was just twenty years old. She must have been very lonely. Her husband was gone for three years.

PART 2: JERKY OLD TIME SILENT MOVIES (TURKEYS, QUAIL

In the 1854 West of Joseph Francl one sees many birds like jerky old time silent movies (turkeys, quail, ducks, geese, snipes, pheasants) and many animals like actors in those movies (buffaloes, elk, wolves) and many fish like swimming silent titles (pike, catfish, perch) and vast lonely areas that are not like movies where no one lives and the road is slender and easy to lose: *We realized that we were wandering. The road we are on looks dim, no one has been over it for a year. There are no human tracks, but there are*

[3]

signs that wolves and larger animals have passed here. An overpowering stillness oppresses us.

It is a land inhabited by sly, dog-stealing Indians who know how to get the best of you, even when you mount a small army and go to their camp and demand the dog back, threatening the Indians with WAR! if they do not return the dog (how very distant this is from Prague, Czechoslovakia, and a brief career in classical music!) but the Indians are crafty in their dog-stealing ways and offer a horse in return for the dog, but work things so that the horse never actually changes hands, and the men return (including Joseph Francl) dogless to their camp and without the promised horse, knowing that they have been had. The dog is lost and the Indians are just too God-damn smart.

The people that Joseph Francl met on his way West are mentally cross-eyed and archetypically funky. I do not think your well-balanced section of society chooses to pioneer the frontier. It is always a breed of strange, half-crazy people who go to make their lives where no one else has lived.

Joseph Francl starts right off in the beginning, I mean, he doesn't fool around, travelling with three insane German brothers and another German who dreams of German military glory and world supremacy.

This was in 1854!

And of course they all got drunk on their first day out and were terribly hung over, including Joseph Francl who cared for his beer and other liquors, too.

[4]

In and out of his travelling vision of the West, wander a cheating landlord, a charlatan doctor, a cynical farmer, *wild, Godless* hunters and trappers whom Joseph Francl thinks would look strange in the streets of Europe: *Their clothing speaks for them. They could not walk through the streets of any European city, nor would they be permitted to do so, without bringing a crowd around them, the members of which would ask each other what sort of comedians are these?*

He meets a smart-assed adulterous wife and her simple good-hearted stupid cuckolded husband, a judge going out to Utah to administer justice and cleanup at the same time with $25,000 worth of dry goods that he's going to sell to the Mormons whom Joseph Francl considers to be an *unchaste breed of humanity*, a hungry Indian chief who did not thank Joseph Francl for giving him dinner, a licentious clergyman and his pretty mistress-cook, a band of extorting Sioux Indians, just back from war with the Pawnees, carrying with them twenty-one Pawnee scalps which they show a great deal of affection toward, and the kind owner of a wagon train that gave Joseph Francl some dinner and some flour when he was very hungry.

In the Placerville gold country of California he met two men who gave him a bad deal on a dry claim and he dealt with merchants that extended credit to him for his unrequited search for wealth while he lived in an abandoned Chinaman's shack, looking for gold, and finally he had to go to work for someone who wasn't very well off himself.

Things just did not work out for Joseph Francl in California, a land that he describes as *this beautiful but unfortunate country.*

And all the time that he was gone his wife Antonia waited in Wisconsin for his return. She was also in poor health. Three years passed. That's a long time for a young woman who's not feeling well.

PART 3: THE LONG DOORS OF JOSEPH FRANCL

We arrived in camp on the third day amid a big rain and thunder storm and supper was served with difficulty. I was just pouring out the tea when I heard—

But we'll never know what Joseph Francl heard because part of his diary was lost right after *when I heard—*

I find the breaks in his diary very beautiful like long poetic pauses where you can hear the innocence of eternity.

Just before *when I heard—*he was working as a cook on a wagon train and there was a lot of Indian trouble. Some Pawnee Indians were really making it hard on them. Most of the Indians didn't have any clothes on. They were running around naked, except for their weapons, and they did not have pleasant ideas in their minds.

. . . *when I heard—*

We'll never know.

When we are returned to his narrative, we find him at the beginning of the Great Plains, and what he heard is lost forever.

The next break in his writing is a chosen one. He is at

[6]

Fort Laramie and he says, *I will not describe the rest of my journey to Salt Lake City, for I do not remember that anything of interest occurred.*

Then suddenly he is in Salt Lake City and nothing is described in between as if the distance from Fort Laramie (over 400 miles) to Salt Lake City were just a door that you opened and stepped through.

Joseph Francl's diary ends with him in the Sierra Mountains, waking up in the morning covered with snow.

And Antonia waited in Wisconsin for her husband, who was Joseph Francl covered with snow, worrying about him, and when he would be back.

Three long years passed.

PART 4: TWO CZECHOSLOVAKIANS LIE BURIED HERE IN AMERICA

Joseph Francl finally returned to Antonia who was now twenty-three years old. She must have been very happy. She probably threw her arms around him and cried.

Then he settled down for a while and they had five more children and he returned to his old Prague musical ways. He taught piano and singing and was the director of the Mendelssohn Singing Society in Watertown, Wisconsin.

He also worked as a county clerk for years and then in 1869 he moved to Crete, Nebraska, and started a general store there in 1870, but business was bad, so in 1874 for some God-damn California dreaming reason, he left his wife Antonia and a bunch of children behind in Crete and returned to Placerville, looking for gold again. This was years after the gold rush was over.

He didn't write about his trip to California this time. He just went there. Of course things didn't work out for him this time either. He even lived in the same Chinaman's shack that he lived in twenty years before.

Joseph Francl was never destined to make anything out of California, so he went to visit his oldest son Fred who was now grown and living up near Walla Walla, Washington, chopping wood for a living.

Fred was the American grandson of a Czechoslovakian brewery and glassworks owner. How distant the seeds of blood are blown over this world.

In the spring of 1875, Joseph Francl walked from Placerville to Portland, Oregon. That's 650 miles of walking. He turned right at the Columbia River and walked up to the Blue Mountains where his son lived.

Working conditions were poor in Washington, so he, his son, and a friend of his son decided to go to California where things might be better (Oh no!) and Joseph Francl was off on his third trip to California.

They travelled on horses, but it was a bad winter and Joseph Francl's son Fred decided to turn back and go by ship to California, leaving his father and his friend to continue on horses to California.

OK: So now it was son by ship and father by horse to California. Things are really getting strange now. The story of Joseph Francl is not an easy one.

Joseph Francl got sick travelling through Oregon, and he didn't eat anything for eleven days and then he was delirious for several days. I do not know what form his delirium took but perhaps Indians and concert halls were a part of it.

Then Joseph Francl got lost from his travelling companion who looked for him, then went for help. When the search party found him a few days later, he was lying facedown in the snow, dead, and he was not unhappy.

In his delirium he probably thought that death was California. He was buried at Fort Klamath, Oregon, on December 10, 1875 in a grave that was lost forever. It was the end of his American childhood.

Antonia Francl died in Crete, Nebraska, on November 21, 1911, and all the waiting that could ever be done was over now.

All the People That
I Didn't Meet and the
Places That I Didn't Go

"I have a short lifeline," she says. "Damn it."

We're lying together under the sheet. It's morning. She's looking at her hand. She's twenty-three: dark hair. She's very carefully looking at her hand.

"Damn it!"

The Japanese Squid Fishermen
Are Asleep Now

That's why I forgot the bottle this morning because the Japanese squid fishermen are asleep and I was thinking about them being asleep.

Last night before I went to bed at one o'clock, I could see them fishing for squid. Their boats were anchored down below on the Pacific Ocean and there were lights shining from the boats. They used the lights to attract squid. The four boats of the Japanese squid fishermen were arranged perfectly like stars in the sky. They were their own constellation.

That's why I forgot the bottle. I thought about them fishing until dawn and maybe having a drink or two before going to sleep. I should have been thinking about the bottle instead of sleeping Japanese squid fishermen.

I brought the bottle to Japan with me a month ago.

[11]

Its history is sort of interesting. One night a few weeks before I left San Francisco for Japan, I was sitting in a bar with some friends and we came up with the idea of writing little messages and putting them in a bottle that I would take with me to Japan and throw into the sea.

The bartender who's a good friend of mine got a very solid empty bottle whose previous occupant had been some Drambuie and we all started writing messages but we didn't show them to each other. As each person wrote a message, he kept it to himself, not showing it to anyone else and then put it in the bottle and after a few hours there were maybe thirty-five or forty messages in the bottle. It resembled the cross-section of an evening in an American bar.

My bartender friend put the cork back in and sealed the bottle with a very sturdy wax that he had with him because he is also a calligrapher and uses a seal to sign his name in wax on the beautiful words that he makes. It was a professional job of bottle sealing. I took the bottle home drunk and happy.

A few weeks later I brought it to Japan with me to throw into the sea where it would drift with the tide and maybe all the way back to America and be found three hundred years later and be quite a media curiosity or just break against a California rock, the pieces of glass sinking to the bottom and the released messages floating a brief lifetime before becoming an indistinguishable part of the tide's residue stranded anonymously on the beach.

So far, so good, except that I forgot the bottle this morning because I was thinking about the sleeping Japanese

[12]

squid fishermen and walked out of the apartment where I am staying here at Ajiro with friends who had rented a boat, so that we could take the bottle out a long ways and throw it into the sea and then do some fishing.

My Japanese friends liked the story of the bottle and looked forward to their part in its voyage. When we arrived at the dock and the waiting boat, they asked me where the bottle was.

I looked very surprised and had to say that I had forgotten it, but the truth was that the bottle was with the sleeping Japanese squid fishermen. The bottle was on a table beside all their beds, waiting for the night to come, so that it could join their constellation.

The Smallest
Snowstorm on Record

The smallest snowstorm on record took place an hour ago in my back yard. It was approximately two flakes. I waited for more to fall, but that was it. The entire storm was just two flakes.

They fell from the sky in a manner reminiscent of the pratfall poignancy of Laurel and Hardy who, come to think of it, the two flakes resembled. It was as if Laurel and Hardy had been turned into snowflakes and starred in the world's smallest snowstorm.

The two flakes seemed to take a long time to fall from the sky with pies in the face, agonizingly funny attempts to maintain dignity in a world that wanted to take it from them, a world that was used to larger snowstorms, two feet or more, and could easily frown upon a two flake storm.

After they did a comedy landing upon snow left over from a dozen storms so far this winter, there was a period of waiting as I looked skyward for more snow, and then realized that the two flakes were a complete storm themselves like Laurel and Hardy.

I went outside and tried to find them. I admired their courage to be themselves in the face of it all. As I was looking for them, I was devising ways to get them into the freezer where they would be comfortable and receive the attention, admiration and accolades they so beautifully deserved.

Have you ever tried to find two snowflakes on a winter landscape that's been covered with snow for months?

I went to the general area where they had landed. I was looking for two snowflakes in a world of billions. Also, there was the matter of stepping on them, which was not a good idea.

It was only a short time before I gave up realizing how hopeless it was. The world's smallest snowstorm was lost

[14]

forever. There was no way to tell the difference between it and everything else.

I like to think that the unique courage of that two flake snowstorm somehow lives on in a world where such things are not always appreciated.

I went back into the house, leaving Laurel and Hardy lost in the snow.

A San Francisco Snake Story

When one thinks of San Francisco, one does not think of snakes. This is a tourist town and people come here to look at French bread. They do not want to see snakes in San Francisco. They would stay at home in the rest of America if the loaves of French bread were replaced by snakes.

But visitors to San Francisco may rest at ease. What I am about to relate is the only San Francisco snake story that I know.

Once I had a beautiful Chinese woman for a friend.

[15]

She was very intelligent and also had an excellent figure whose primary focus was her breasts. They were large and well shaped. They gardened and harvested much attention wherever she went.

It is interesting that I was more attracted to her intelligence than I was to her body. I find intelligence in women to be an aphrodisiac and she was one of the most intelligent people I have ever known.

Everybody else would be looking at her breasts and I would be looking at her mind, which was architecturally clear and analytical like winter starlight.

What does a beautiful Chinese woman's mind have to do with a story about snakes in San Francisco you are probably asking about now with a rising temperature of impatience.

One day we went to a store that sold snakes. It was some kind of reptile gardens and we were just walking around San Francisco with no particular destination in mind and we happened upon this professional den of snakes.

So we went in.

The store was filled with hundreds of snakes.

Every place you looked there were snakes.

After you noticed, and I might add very shortly after you noticed the snakes, you noticed the smell of snake shit. To my recollection, which cannot be taken as gospel if you are a serious student of snakes, it smelled like a sinking dead lazy sweet doughnut about the size of a moving van, but it somehow was not bad enough to make us leave the place.

[16]

We were fascinated by this dirty snakehouse.

Why didn't the owners clean up after the snakes?

Snakes don't want to live in their own shit. They'd sooner forget the whole God-damn thing. Go back where they came from in the first place.

The dirty snakeshop had snakes from Africa and South America and Asia and from all over the world lying there in shit. They all needed one-way airplane tickets.

In the middle of this snake horror there was a huge cage full of very calm white mice who would all eventually end up as the smell in that place.

The Chinese woman and I walked about looking at the snakes. We were appalled and fascinated at the same time by this reptilian hell.

We ended up at a case with two cobras in it and they were both staring at her breasts. The heads of the snakes were very close to the glass. They looked just like the way they do in the movies but the movies leave out the smell of snake shit.

The Chinese woman was not very tall, 5-1 or so. The two stinking cobras stared at her breasts that were only a few inches away. Maybe that is why I always liked her mind.

Football

The confidence that he got by being selected all-state in football lasted him all of his life. He was killed in an automobile accident when he was twenty-two. He was buried on a rainy afternoon. Halfway through the burial service the minister forgot what he was talking about. Everybody stood there at the grave waiting for him to remember.

Then he remembered.

"This young man," he said. "Played football."

Ice Age Cab Company

These mountains of Montana are endlessly changing, minute to minute, nothing remains the same. It is the work of sun and wind and snow. It is the play of clouds and shadows.

I am staring at the mountains again.

It is the time of another sunset. This one is muted. I expected to watch a different sunset when I left the house and came out here to this room sitting in the top of a red barn with a large window facing the mountains.

I expected a clear sharp sunset, analytical in its perception of this the first snowy day of the autumn down here in the valley:

. . . October 10, 1977.

We went to sleep last night with it snowing, but now the sunset is changing again, minute to minute, taking on a different character. The mute quality is giving way to a vague sharpness like a knife that can cut some things but

[19]

can't cut other things. It can cut a peach but it can't cut an apple.

There was a great old woman who used to run the taxi-cab company in town which was only a little more than one cab. You might say that the whole cab company was one cab+ and not be far from the truth.

Anyway, last year she was driving me out here and high white clouds had gone into partnership with a sharp June sun and their business was rapid, dramatic light changes going on in the mountains.

We were of course talking about ice ages.

She liked to talk about ice ages. It was her favorite topic. She finished saying something about ice ages by changing the subject to the light patterns going on in the mountains.

". . . ice ages!" she said, dramatically bringing to an end the conversation about ice ages. Then her voice soft-ened. "These mountains," she said. "I've lived here for over fifty years and maybe looked at the mountains a mil-lion times and they've never looked the same way twice. They're always different, changing."

When she started talking about the mountains, they looked one way and when she finished talking about them, they looked another way.

I guess that's what I'm trying to say about this sunset.

"Different, changing."

Shrine of Carp

The bars are closing in Shibuya on a Friday night and thousands of people are pouring out into the streets like happy drunken toothpaste, laughing and speaking Japanese.

The traffic is very heavy with full taxis. It is well known that Shibuya can be a very difficult place to get a taxicab on a Friday or Saturday night. Sometimes it can be almost impossible, only fate and the direct intervention of the gods will secure you a taxicab.

I stand there in Shibuya in the middle of this gigantic party of Japanese. I feel no anxiety to go home because I am alone. When I get home an empty bed in a hotel room waits for me like a bridge to lonely and solitary sleep.

So I just stand there as peaceful as a banana because that's what I look like in this all-Japanese crowd. Every taxi that comes by me is full in the traffic that's barely moving. Ahead of me I can see empty cabs, but they are seized instantly as soon as they appear.

I don't care.

I am not really going anyplace that counts, not like the many young lovers that I see around me who are on their way to happy drunken fucking.

Let them have the cabs.

They are a blessing from me to them.

I was once young myself.

Then I see an empty cab headed toward me and for some strange reason all the lovers look away and I automatically raise my hand beckoning toward the cab. It is not that I want the cab. It's just done out of unconscious habit. I have no interest in stealing their cab.

When a person feels like that, of course, the taxi stops and I get into it. Kindness can only go so far. It is a privately-owned cab because its interior reflects the personality of the cab driver and shows the professional pride he takes in owning his own cab.

I tell the driver in Japanese where I am going and we start on our way. Still surprised by the cab stopping, it takes me a minute or so to become totally aware of the contents of the taxi. When I get in I can see that something is very unusual about the cab, far beyond the obvious personality touches that driver-owned taxis have.

Then, as they say, it dawns on me in the bar-closing traffic of Shibuya where I am actually at. I'm not in a taxicab. I am in a shrine of carp. The taxi is filled with drawings, photographs and even paintings of carp. In the backseat there are two gold-framed paintings of carp. One of them is beside each door.

Carp are swimming everywhere in the taxi.

"Carp," I say in English to the driver, hoping that means something to him. I don't know the Japanese word for carp.

"Hai," he says in Japanese which means yes. Then I have a feeling that he knows the word for carp in every language on this earth, even in Eskimo where there are no carp, only icebergs and such. The man really likes carp.

I take a good look at him.

He's a happy and jovial man.

I remember that carp stands for good luck in Japanese and I am in a moving shrine of carp, going in and out of the Japanese love-traffic. It all makes sense. I see young lovers in cabs all around us on their way to pleasure and passion. We are swimming among them like good luck.

Meat

A man is staring at meat. He is so intently staring at meat that his immediate surroundings have become the shadow of a mirage.

He is wearing a wedding ring.

He is perhaps in his early sixties.

He is well dressed.

There simply are no clues to why he is staring at meat. People walk by him on the sidewalk. He does not notice them. Some people have to step around him.

The meat is his only attention.

He's motionless. His arms are at his side. There's no expression on his face.

He is staring into the open door of a meat market locker where whole sides of beef are hanging from hooks. They are in a row like cold red dominoes.

I walk past him and turn around and look at him and then want to know why he is standing there and I walk back and try to see what he is seeing as I walk past him.

There has to be something else, but I'm wrong again in this life.

Nothing but meat.

Umbrellas

I have never been able to understand umbrellas because I don't care if I get wet. Umbrellas have always been a mystery to me because I can't understand why they appear just before it starts to rain. The rest of the time they are vacant from the landscape as if they had never existed. Maybe the umbrellas live by themselves in little apartments under Tokyo.

Do the umbrellas know that it is going to rain? because I know that people don't know. The weatherman says that it will rain tomorrow but it doesn't and you don't see a single God-damn umbrella. Then the weatherman says that it will be a sunshiny day and suddenly there are umbrellas everywhere you look, and a few moments later, it starts raining like hell.

Who are these umbrellas?

A Death in Canada

There is not much to talk about today here in Tokyo. I feel very dull like a rusty knife in the kitchen of a weed-dominated monastery that was abandoned because everybody was too bored to say their prayers any more, so they went someplace else two hundred years ago and started different lives that led them all to the grave, anyway, a place where we are all going.

A few moments ago somebody died in their sleep in Canada. It was a very easy death. They just won't wake up tomorrow morning. Their death will not affect the results of anything going on in Japan because nobody will know about it, not a single person out of 114,000,000 people.

The Canadian corpse will be buried the day after tomorrow. By any standard it will be a modest funeral. The minister will have a hard time keeping his mind on the sermon. He would just about prefer to be doing anything else than giving this sermon.

He is almost angry at the corpse lying a few feet away in a cheap coffin. At one point he feels like grabbing the corpse and shaking it like a child that's done a bad thing while his voice continues droning out: "We are all but mortal flesh on a perilous journey from birth to . . ." he looks over at the corpse he has to refrain from keeping his hands off . . . "death."

A few hours after the corpse is safely in the ground, he will be home drinking a water glass of sherry in his locked-door study.

None of this will have any effect on Japan. No one will ever know about it.

This evening somebody will die in their sleep in Kyoto. They will turn over in bed and just die. Their body will slowly grow cold and Canada will not declare a day of national mourning.

Autumn Trout Gathering

Time to go fishing . . .

It is October again in Montana and I have been away again, Japan, etc., but I am back here again in the Rockies. As I am writing this: I'm thinking about the word again. I am thinking that it is a relative of the word rain. They have so much in common. When it starts raining it is a process of again and again lasting for minutes, hours or days.

For my autumn's fishing I will need a new license and some flies and leaders, so I go to a fishing tackle store and renew myself again as a fisherman.

I love fishing tackle stores.

They are cathedrals of childhood romance, for I spent thousands of hours worshipping the possibilities of rods and reels that led like a religion to rivers and lakes waiting to be fished in the imagination where I would fish every drop of water on this planet.

The next day I am getting myself ready to go fishing. I select a 7½ foot rod to try my luck with on a spring creek.

I get my hip boots and fishing vest.

I plan the flies that I will take with me. My Japanese wife is carefully but casually watching my preparations which I perform with an obvious enthusiasm.

When I am ready to go, time to go fishing, she says, "Don't forget to take some Kleenex."

"What?" I ask, startled because I have been fishing for over a third of a century and Kleenex has not played a part in my fishing.

"Take some Kleenex with you."

"What?"

I am definitely on the defensive, trying to deal with a brand-new aspect of fishing, something that had never crossed my mind before.

"You might sneeze."

I think about it.

She is right.

Harmonica High

At odd moments like a brief bird, a sudden and enchanting obsession has flown into my mind and sat there for a while in the branches of my intelligence staring at me with a happy expression on its face and then flown away to return again for short visits later on. It always keeps coming back.

In other words: Harmonica High!

I daydream about a high school where everybody plays the harmonica: the students, the teachers, the principal, the janitor and the cook in the cafeteria.

Everybody has their own harmonica playing away from the time school opens until it closes. Harmonica High is a happy school where the only subject taught is playing the harmonica, and after school the students leave, taking with them harmonica homework.

Harmonica High doesn't have a football team, a basketball team or a baseball team. They have harmonica teams that eagerly accept all challengers and never lose.

On the first day of school every September the incoming freshmen are given harmonicas and on the last day of school the graduating seniors get to keep them because the harmonicas are their diplomas.

There are beautiful green trees that grow around Harmonica High and from September until June there's always a harmonica breeze in the leaves and you can hear the school from a mile away.

It's a different concept of education that can only be described as Harmonica High.

Winter Vacation

Driving to town: the graves have turned to powdered wind and swirl gently across the road in front of us, but it's nothing to be afraid of. It's just a typical Montana winter day passing the cemetery whose only punctuation are bunches of plastic flowers sticking out of the snow.

The cemetery is one of the modern kind without tombstones or crosses. Designed for efficiency like a refrigerator, it has flat metal markers planted in the ground, so the only evidence of the graves is the plastic flowers and powdered wind blowing off the graves and caressing the road. A wind down from the mountains has allowed the graves to escape their solemn moorings.

Driving by: I think the graves are almost frolicking, glad to be free of their anchors, ports of entry, sailing schedules and silent cargo.

The graves are free this winter day, happy.

The Purpose

There is no reason for the telephone to be ringing in the middle of the night on a Sunday and to keep ringing.

The coffee shop is very closed.

The place does not sell coffee by the cup but by the pound, so there's nobody sitting in there drinking coffee who needs a telephone call.

It is a place where they roast beans and sell them that way or ground to your desire, what you want a cup of coffee to do, what you expect from the beans. Maybe you like Shakespeare. Somebody else might care for Laurel and Hardy.

But the telephone keeps ringing.

Nobody's inside except for the coffee roasting machinery which looks as if its actual purpose is something medieval that has nothing to do with roasting coffee beans, something ninth century and up to no good.

Nearby are silent sacks of beans waiting to be roasted. They come from South America and Africa, places like that, faraway, mysterious, but not as mysterious as the telephone ringing. The shop has been closed since 6 p.m.

Saturday.

It is now 2 a.m.

Sunday.

The telephone continues ringing.

Who is on the other end of the line? What are they thinking as they listen to the telephone ring in an empty coffee shop where it will not be answered until Monday at 8 a.m.? Are they sitting or standing while the telephone rings? Is it a man or a woman?

At least, we know one thing: They've found something to do.

The Irrevocable Sadness of
Her Thank You

She won't escape. I won't let her escape. I don't want her lost forever because frankly I am one of the few people on this planet who gives a damn about her other than her friends and family if she has any.

I am the only American from a land of 218,000,000 Americans who cares about her. Nobody from the Soviet Union or China or Norway or France cares
. . . or the entire continent of Africa.

I was waiting at Harajuku Station for the Yamanote Line train to take me home to Shinjuku. The platform faced a lush green hillside: deep green grass with lots of bushes and trees, as always a pleasant sight here in Tokyo.

I didn't notice her waiting for the train on the platform with me, though I'm certain she was there, probably standing right beside me, and that's why I am writing this story.

The Yamanote train came.

It's green, too, but not lush, almost tropical like the hill beside the station. The train is sort of metallically worn out. The train is faded like an old man's dreams of long ago springs when he was perhaps even young and all he had in front of him is behind him now.

We got on the train.

All the seats were occupied and we had to stand and then I noticed her standing beside me because she was tall for a Japanese woman, maybe 5-7. She was wearing a simple white dress and there was a very calm, almost serene feeling of sadness about her.

Her height and sadness captured my attention and for the six or seven minutes that it takes to get to Shinjuku, she completely possessed my mind and now permanently occupies an important place there as these words bear witness.

At the next stop a man sitting in front of me got up and the seat was vacant. I could feel her waiting for me to sit down, but I didn't. I just stood there waiting for her to sit down. There was no one else standing near us, so it was obvious that I was giving the seat to her.

I was thinking to her: *Please sit down. I want you to have the seat.* She continued standing beside me, staring at the empty seat.

I was just about to point at the seat and say in Japanese *"dozo"* which means please, when a man sitting next to

[34]

the empty seat slid over, taking it and then offering her his seat and she sat down in his seat, but she turned to me as she sat down and said "thank you" to me in English. All of this took maybe twenty seconds from the time the seat in front of me was vacated and the woman was sitting down in the seat next to it.

This complicated little life ballet movement started my mind ringing like a sunken bell at the bottom of the Pacific Ocean during a great earthquake tearing cracks in the ocean floor, starting a tidal wave headed toward the nearest shore, maybe thousands of miles away: India.

The bell was ringing with the irrevocable sadness of her thank you. I had never heard two words spoken so sadly before. Though the earthquake of their first utterance is gone now, I am still in the power of its hundreds of aftershocks.

Thank you, thank you, thank you, thank you, thank you, thank you, thank you, thank you, after shocking over and over again in my mind, *thank you, thank you, thank you, thank you, thank you, thank you, thank you, thank you.*

I watched her sitting there for the few minutes until Shinjuku Station. She took out a book and started reading it. I couldn't tell what kind of book it was. I don't know if it was philosophy or a cheap romance. I have no idea of the quality of her intelligence, but her reading the book gave me the opportunity to look at her openly without making her feel uncomfortable.

She never looked up from the book.

[35]

She was wearing a simple white dress, which I think was not very expensive. I don't think that it cost very much money at all. The design was starkly plain and the material was modest in thread count and quality. The dress was not fashionably plain. It was really plain.

She was wearing very cheap, white plastic shoes that looked as if they had come from the bargain bin of a shoe store.

She was wearing faded pink socks. They made me feel sad. I had never looked at a pair of socks before and felt sad, but these socks made me feel very sad, though that sadness was only 1,000,000th the sadness of her thank you. Those socks were the happiest day of my entire life compared to her thank you.

The only jewelry she was wearing was a little red plastic ring. It looked like something you'd get in a box of Cracker Jacks.

She had to have had a purse to take the book out of because she wasn't carrying the book when she sat down and there were no pockets in her dress, but I can't remember anything about the purse. Perhaps, this was all that I could take.

Every living system has its limits.

Her purse was beyond the limits of my life.

About her age and appearance, as I said earlier, she was about 5-7, tall for a Japanese woman, and she was young and sad. She could have been anywhere between 18 and 32. It's hard to tell a Japanese woman's age.

She was young and sad, going to where I will never

know, still sitting there on the train, reading a book when I got off at Shinjuku Station, with her thank you like a ghost forever ringing in my mind.

No Hunting
Without Permission

October 21, 1978: Yesterday I didn't do anything. It was like a play written for a weedy vacant lot where a theater would be built one hundred years after I am dead performed by actors whose great grandparents haven't even been born yet. If I were keeping a diary, yesterday's entry would have gone something like this:

Dear Diary, I put up a no hunting sign today because tomorrow is the first day of hunting season and I don't want some out of state hunters driving a station wagon with Louisiana license plates to stop and shoot a moose in my back yard.

[37]

I also went to a party. I was in a shitty off-angle wrong mood and said the same five boring sentences to forty different, totally unsuspecting and innocent people. It took me three hours to get around to everybody and there were very long pauses between sentences.

One sentence was an incoherent comment about the State of the Union. I substituted an obscure California weather pattern in place of a traditional Montana weather pattern to use as a metaphor about inflation.

What I said made absolutely no sense whatsoever and when I finished nobody asked me to elaborate. A few people said that they needed some more wine and excused themselves to go get some, though I could see that they still had plenty of wine left in their glasses.

I also told everybody that I had seen a moose in my back yard, right outside the kitchen window. Then I did not give any more details. I just stood there staring at them while they waited patiently for me to continue talking about the moose, but that was it.

A little old lady told me that she had to go to the toilet. Later on during the party every time I was in her vicinity, she immediately started talking desperately to the closest person.

A man I told my moose story to said, "Was that the same moose you told me about yesterday?" I looked a little shocked and then said, "Yes." The shocked expression slowly changed into one of serene bewilderment.

I think my mind is going. It is changing into a cranial junkyard. I have a huge pile of rusty tin cans the size of

[38]

Mount Everest and about a million old cars that are going nowhere except between my ears.

I stayed at the party for three hours, though it seemed closer to a light-year of one-sentence moose stories.

Then I went home and watched *Fantasy Island* on television. As a sort of laststand nervous spiritual pickup, I called a friend in California on the telephone during a commercial. We had a very low-keyed conversation during the commercial. He was not really that interested in talking to me. He was more interested in doing something else.

As we struggled through the conversation, like quicksand, I wondered what the first thing he would do after I hung up. Maybe he would pour himself a stiff drink or he would call somebody interesting on the telephone and tell them how boring I had become.

At one point toward the end of our thousand-mile little chat, I said, "Well, I've just been fishing and writing. I've written seven little short stories this week."

"Nobody cares," my friend said. And he was right.

I started to tell him that I had seen a moose in my back yard but I changed my mind. I would save it for another time. I did not want to use up my best material right away. You've got to think of the future.

OPEN

Once she owned a Chinese restaurant and she worked very hard to get it. I think she spent her whole life earning the money. The location had not been a restaurant before, so she had to start from the very beginning and create a restaurant from a place that had been an Italian men's clothing store for years with a clientele that was exclusively old men. The store finally closed when all its customers died.

Then the woman came along and made it into a Chinese restaurant. She replaced somber dark suits with fried rice and chow mein.

She was a small middle-aged Chinese woman who had once been very good looking, probably beautiful. She decorated the restaurant herself. It was a comfortable little world that reflected the values of the Chinese lower middle-class. There were bright and cheerful Chinese lanterns and inexpensive scrolls that had birds painted on them and little glass knickknacks from Hong Kong.

She had to build the restaurant from the very beginning, including lowering the ceiling and panelling the walls and carpeting the floor. There was also, and this is a big also, putting in the kitchen and creating two bathrooms. None of that is cheap.

She put her life's savings into the restaurant and hoped for the best, probably prayed for the best. Unfortunately, it was not to come her way. Who knows why a restaurant fails? She had good food at reasonable prices and a good location with lots of foot traffic, but people just didn't want to eat there.

I went there a couple of times a week and became friends with her. She was a very nice woman. I slowly watched her restaurant fade away. Often when I ate there, there were only two or three other people in the restaurant. Sometimes there were none.

After a while she took to looking at the door a lot. She sat at an empty table, surrounded by empty tables and watched the door, waiting for customers that never came.

She would talk to me about it. "I can't understand it," she would say. "This is a good restaurant. There are a lot of people walking by. I don't understand."

I didn't understand either and when I ate there, I gradually became a shadow of her, watching the door, hoping for customers.

She put up a huge sign in the front window that said OPEN. By then it was too late, nothing could help. I went away to Japan for a few months. When I came back the restaurant was closed. She had run out of time, staring at the front door while it grew cobwebs.

I didn't see her again for about two years and then I bumped into her one day on the street. We said our hellos and she asked me how I was and I said, "Fine," and she told me that she was fine. "You know I lost the restaurant," she said.

Then she turned and pointed her hand down the street toward a neon sign two blocks away that jutted out, breaking the anonymity of the block. The sign told us that the Adams and White Mortuary was located there.

"I've been working for Adams and White since the restaurant failed," she said, her voice was almost desperate and suddenly she seemed very small like a frightened child, just waking up from a nightmare and trying to talk about it while it was still so vivid that the child couldn't tell the difference between it and reality.

Spiders Are in the House

It is autumn. Spiders are in the house. They have come in from the cold. They want to spend the winter in here. I don't blame them. It's cold out there. I like spiders and welcome them. They're OK in my book. I've always liked spiders, even when I was a child. I was afraid of other things, like my playmates, but I wasn't afraid of spiders.

Why?

I don't know: just because. Maybe I was a spider in another life. Maybe I wasn't. Who cares? There are spiders living comfortably in my house while the wind howls outside. They aren't bothering anybody. If I were a fly, I'd have second thoughts but I'm not, so I don't.

. . . nice spiders protected from the wind.

Very Good Dead Friends

One day in his life he realized that he had more very good dead friends than he had living ones. When he first realized this, he spent an afternoon turning thousands of people in his mind like pages in the telephone book to see if he was right.

He was, and he didn't know how to feel about it. At first he felt sad. Then the sadness slowly turned into feeling nothing at all and that felt better, like not being aware of the wind blowing on a very windy day.

Your mind someplace else,
No wind there.

What Are You Going to Do with 390 Photographs of Christmas Trees?

I don't know. But it seemed like the thing to do in that first week in January 1964, and I got two other people to join me. One of them wants to remain anonymous, and that's all right.

I think we were still in shock over President Kennedy's assassination. Perhaps that had something to do with all those photographs of Christmas trees.

The Christmas of 1963 looked terrible, illuminated by all the flags in America hanging at half-mast week after week in December like a tunnel of mourning.

I was living by myself in a very strange apartment where I was taking care of an aviary for some people who were in Mexico. I fed the birds every day and changed their water and had a little vacuum cleaner to tidy up the aviary when it was needed.

I ate dinner by myself on Christmas day. I had some hot dogs and beans and drank a bottle of rum with Coca-Cola. It was a lonesome Christmas and President Kennedy's murder was almost like one of those birds that I had to feed every day.

The only reason I am mentioning this is to kind of set the psychological framework for 390 photographs of Christmas trees. A person does not get into this sort of thing without sufficient motivation.

Late one evening I was walking home from visiting some people on Nob Hill. We had sat around drinking cup after cup of coffee until our nerves had become lionesque.

I left around midnight and walked down a dark and silent street toward home, and I saw a Christmas tree abandoned next to a fire hydrant.

The tree had been stripped of its decorations and lay there sadly like a dead soldier after a losing battle. A week before it had been a kind of hero.

Then I saw another Christmas tree with a car half-parked on it. Somebody had left their tree in the street and the car had accidentally run over it. The tree was certainly a long way from a child's loving attention. Some of the branches were sticking up through the bumper.

It was that time of the year when people in San Fran-

[45]

cisco get rid of their Christmas trees by placing them in the streets or vacant lots or wherever they can get rid of them. It is the journey away from Christmas.

Those sad and abandoned Christmas trees really got on my conscience. They had provided what they could for that assassinated Christmas and now they were just being tossed out to lie there in the street like bums.

I saw dozens of them as I walked home through the beginning of a new year. There are people who just chuck their Christmas trees right out the front door. A friend of mine tells a story about walking down the street on December 26th and having a Christmas tree go whistling right by his ear, and hearing a door slam. It could have killed him.

There are others who go about abandoning their Christmas trees with stealth and skill. That evening I *almost* saw somebody put a Christmas tree out, but not quite. They were invisible like the Scarlet Pimpernel. I could *almost* hear the Christmas tree being put out.

I went around a corner and there in the middle of the street lay the tree, but nobody was around. There are always people who do a thing with greatness, no matter what it is.

When I arrived at home I went to the telephone and called up a friend of mine who is a photographer and accessible to the strange energies of the Twentieth Century. It was almost one o'clock in the morning. I had awakened him and his voice was a refugee from sleep.

"Who is it?" he said.

[46]

"Christmas trees," I said.

"What?"

"Christmas trees."

"Is that you, Richard?" he asked.

"Yeah."

"What about them?"

"Christmas is only skin deep," I said. "Why don't we take hundreds of pictures of Christmas trees that are abandoned in the streets? We'll show the despair and abandonment of Christmas by the way people throw their trees out."

"Might as well do that as anything else," he said. "I'll start tomorrow during my lunch hour."

"I want you to photograph them just like dead soldiers," I said. "Don't touch or pose them. Just photograph them the way they fell."

The next day he took photographs of Christmas trees during his lunch hour. He worked at Macy's then and went up on the slopes of Nob Hill and Chinatown and took pictures of Christmas trees there.

1, 2, 3, 4, 5, 9, 11, 14, 21, 28, 37, 52, 66.

I called him that evening.

"How did it go?"

"Wonderful," he said.

The next day he took more photographs of Christmas trees during his lunch hour.

72, 85, 117, 128, 137.

I called him up that evening, too.

"How did it go?"

"Couldn't be better," he said. "I've almost got 150 of them."

"Keep up the good work," I said. I was busy lining up a car for the weekend, so that we would have mobility to take more Christmas tree photographs.

I thought we should get a good sampling of what San Francisco had to offer in the way of abandoned Christmas trees.

The person who drove us around the next day desires to remain anonymous. He is afraid that he would lose his job and face financial and social pressures if it got out that he worked with us that day.

The next morning we started out and we drove all over San Francisco taking photographs of abandoned Christmas trees. We faced the project with the zest of a trio of revolutionaries.

142, 159, 168, 175, 183.

We would be driving along and spot a Christmas tree lying perhaps in the front yard of somebody's lovely house in Pacific Heights or beside an Italian grocery store in North Beach. We would suddenly stop and jump out and rush over to the Christmas tree and start taking pictures from every angle.

The simple people of San Francisco probably thought that we were all completely deranged: bizarre. We were traffic stoppers in the classic tradition.

199, 215, 227, 233, 245.

We met the poet Lawrence Ferlinghetti out walking his dog on Potrero Hill. He saw us jump out of the car and immediately start taking pictures of a fallen Christmas tree lying on the sidewalk.

277, 278, 279, 280, 281.

As he walked by, he said, "Taking pictures of Christmas trees?"

"Sort of," we said and all thinking paranoiacally: *Does he know what we are doing?* We wanted to keep it a big secret. We thought we really had something good going and it needed the right amount of discretion before it was completed.

So the day passed and our total of Christmas tree photographs crept over the 300 mark.

"Don't you think we have enough now?" Bob said.

"No, just a few more," I said.

317, 332, 345, 356, 370.

"Now?" Bob said.

We had driven all the way across San Francisco again and were on Telegraph Hill, climbing down a broken staircase to a vacant lot where somebody had tossed a Christmas tree over a cyclone fence. The tree had the same candor as Saint Sebastian, arrows and all.

"No, just a few more," I said.

386, 387, 388, 389, 390.

"We must have enough now," Bob said.

"I think so," I said.

We were all very happy. That was the first week of 1964. It was a strange time in America.

The Pacific Ocean

Today I thought about the Pacific Ocean on the platform at Shinjuku Station, waiting for the Yamanote Line train.

I don't know why I thought about the Pacific engulfing and devouring itself, the ocean eating itself and getting smaller and smaller until it was the size of Rhode Island but still eating away and getting smaller and smaller, an insatiable appetite, getting smaller and smaller and heavier and heavier, the entire weight of the Pacific Ocean into a smaller and smaller form until the Pacific Ocean was concentrated into a single drop weighing trillions of tons. Then the train came and I might add, it was about time.

I left the Pacific Ocean behind on the platform underneath a candy bar wrapper.

Another Texas Ghost Story

She is brushing his hair gently with her hand. She is caressing his face gently with her hand. This is a ghost story. It begins in West Texas in the early 1930s at night in a large house full of sleeping people out in the hill country and will eventually end in 1970 at a picnic gathering of middle-aged people.

She is standing beside his bed. He is fifteen years old and almost asleep. She opens the door and comes into his room. When she opens the door it doesn't make a sound. She walks silently over to him. The floor doesn't creak. He's so sleepy that he isn't afraid. She is an old woman wearing a very careful nightgown. She stands beside him. Her hair flows down to her waist. It is white with faded yellow in it as if her hair had once been singed by fire. This is all that is left of having been a golden blonde woman in the 1890s . . . perhaps even a West Texas belle with many suitors.

He stares at her.

He knows that she is a ghost but he is too sleepy to be afraid. He has spent the day putting twelve hours of hay into the barn. Every muscle in his body is beautifully exhausted and abstract.

She touches his hair gently with her hand. Her hand is delicate and he isn't afraid of it. Then she caresses his face gently with her hand. It isn't warm but it isn't cold either. Her hand possesses an existence between life and death.

She smiles at him. He's so tired that he almost smiles back. She leaves the room and he falls asleep. His dreams are not unpleasant. They are a floating bridge to his mother who wakes him up in the morning by loudly opening the door to his bedroom and yelling, "Time to get up! Breakfast is on the table!"

He is silent at the kitchen table. His brothers and sisters are chattering away and his father hasn't said a word while carefully drinking a cup of stoic coffee. His father never talks at the kitchen table, even when it's dinner and there's company. People have gotten used to it.

The boy thinks about the ghost as he eats thick slices of bacon and eggs scrambled in the fat and nibbles on a jalapeño pepper. He really likes jalapeños, the hotter the better.

He does not mention the ghost to anyone at the table. He doesn't want them to think that he is crazy and the years pass and he grows up in that house with his two sisters and two brothers and his mother and his father and the ghost.

[52]

She visits him five or six times a year. There is no pattern to the visits. She doesn't come every May or September or the third of July. She just comes when she wants to, but it averages five or six times a year. She never frightens him and almost seems to love him but they never have anything to say to each other.

It's hard to make a living in that part of Texas in those days, so eventually the family grows up and scatters away from that house and it becomes just another abandoned old house in West Texas.

One sister goes to live in Houston and a brother to Oklahoma City and another sister marries a mechanic and he has a filling station in Las Vegas, New Mexico.

His father dies of a heart attack one rainy afternoon in San Angelo, Texas, and his mother goes to live in an old-folks home in Abilene, Texas, because her sister lives nearby, and one of his brothers gets a job in Canada, and his other brother is killed in an automobile accident in 1943 while in the Air Force stationed at Amarillo, Texas.

Then there is himself: He marries his high school sweetheart and lives in Brownwood, Texas, for three years, working at a feed store.

He is drafted into the infantry and fights in Italy and later on is a part of the Normandy Landing on D-Day 1944 and is wounded once, not seriously, shrapnel in the leg and rises to the rank of sergeant because so many men in his company are killed in a fire fight with some Waffen SS troops on the border of Germany.

He comes back from the war and goes to college on the

[53]

GI Bill for two years at the University of Texas in Austin, majoring in business administration, then drops out of college and works as a cigarette salesman for a few years until by a fluke he gets involved in selling television sets and eventually has a little TV store of his own in Austin.

They have two children: a girl named Joan and a boy Robert.

The old house just continues to stand out there in West Texas: abandoned, a monument to the growing years of an American family. Its dark outline stands against the sunset and the wind bangs something that is loose on the house.

And on . . . and on . . . and on (*years passing, life being lived, problems, good times, bills, etc., the children growing up and getting married . . . on, etc., on*) until he is fifty-three years old at a family reunion picnic with his brother and his two sisters sitting alone together at a wooden table outside in the Texas afternoon, but their mother couldn't come because she's just too old and doesn't recognize them any more. Her sister stopped visiting her last year because it broke her heart to see her that way.

It is at a picnic table covered with plates of barbecue and salad, roast young goat, jalapeños and bottles of Pearl beer that the truth is finally revealed.

He's had four Pearl beers and is talking very affectionately about the old homestead way back there in the 1930s when he finally blurts out, "Did you know that I saw a ghost in that house? There was a ghost there."

Everybody stops eating and drinking and looks at one

[54]

another without really looking at one another. The table is very silent. His oldest sister, fifty-five, puts her fork down.

Then his brother says, "I thought I was the only one who saw a ghost there. I was afraid to mention it. I thought you would all think that I was crazy. Was it the ghost of an old woman with long hair? Was she wearing a nightgown?"

"Yes, that's her."

There is more silence and one of the sisters breaks it by saying, "I saw her, too. She used to come and stand by my bed and touch my hair. I was afraid to tell."

Then they all turn toward the remaining sister who just nods her head slowly. They sit there. Texas children are playing in the background. Their voices are running and happy.

He reaches over and takes his bottle of Pearl beer and holds it out in a toasting motion toward an abandoned house a hundred miles away and says, "Here's to her and to all of us these many years later."

This is the end of a ghost story.

There Is No Dignity,
Only the Windswept Plains
of Ankona

There is no dignity, only the windswept plains of Ankona, he thought as he looked at the calendar and wondered if the year 3021 would be as boring as the year 3020. That could not be possible, he thought, but then he reconsidered the past. The year 3019 had been just as boring as 3018 and it had been the same as 3017. There was no difference between them. They were all twin years of each other.

He examined the past very carefully in his mind and the years had all been very boring ever since he had come to Ankona in 2751 as an experiment to see if a human being could live on the windswept plains for 500 years by himself.

Well, they could God-damn it! he thought, and then tried not to think about the 231 years he had left before the experiment would be completed.

He would like to have met the mastermind who thought up this thing, but the sound of the wind gradually silenced his mind and its anger until he could hear nothing but the wind blowing across the plains of Ankona.

The Tomb of
the Unknown Friend

I saw somebody on the street yesterday that I almost knew very well. It was a man with a kind and interesting face. Too bad we had never met before. We might have been very close friends if only we had met. When I saw him I almost felt like stopping and suggesting that we have a drink and talk about old times, mutual friends and aquaintances: Whatever happened to so and so? and do you remember the night when we . . . ?

The only thing missing was that we had shared no old times together to talk about because you have to meet somebody before you can do that.

The man walked by me without any recognizing expression. My face wore the same mask, but inside I felt as if I almost knew him. It was really a shame that the only thing that separated us from being good friends was the stupid fact that we had never met.

We both disappeared in opposite directions that swallowed any possibility of friendship.

Cooking Spaghetti Dinner in Japan

Yesterday, being yesterday in Tokyo, I cooked a spaghetti dinner for some Japanese friends. I bought the ingredients in a supermarket that specializes in food for foreigners.

These are the things that I bought:

[58]

tomato paste,
tomato sauce,
green and red peppers,
mushrooms,
sweet basil,
a can of pitted black olives,
pasta,
olive oil,
400 grams of hamburger meat,
some butter,
two bottles of red wine,
and Parmesan cheese.

I took the ingredients to a Japanese friend's house and she had the rest of the things that I needed:

3 yellow onions,
oregano,
parsley,
sugar,
salt and pepper,
garlic.

And then I started cooking spaghetti.

I chopped, opened and mixed together until there was the smell of spaghetti coming from the kitchen. It smelled just like dozens of American kitchens where I have cooked spaghetti for over twenty years except there was one thing different: a few feet away from my cooking was a bucket of water filled with tiny live eels.

I had never cooked spaghetti before with eels for company. The eels swam in circles like science-fiction children of spaghetti.

The Beacon

I wonder if he jumped off the Golden Gate Bridge. The details of him being there are unreal, fragmented and seem to be further away than they actually were.

He was simultaneously a few feet away from me and a mile away. He was standing on the other side of the railing, facing San Francisco, ready to jump.

There were five or six other people standing like extras in the background of this tapestry. I think that he had just climbed over the railing. Soon there would be a lot more people sewn to it like strange buttons, some out of compassion, others from morbid curiosity.

He was a man in his early twenties, wearing a classic Clark Gable *It-Happened-One-Night* undershirt. He had taken his coat and shirt off. They were piled neatly beside the railing. His mother would have been proud of him.

He was very pale, white like the idea of frost and seemed

to be in shock as if he had just seen somebody jump off the Golden Gate Bridge.

I was in a car with two friends crossing the bridge and saw this as we drove by in the traffic. I felt as if we should stop and try to help him, but I knew that we couldn't because it would only make things worse and add to the traffic jam already in his mind.

What could be done right now was being done.

I don't know why he wanted to kill himself but I didn't want him to do it and I couldn't do anything about it.

The young man was like a lonely beacon of humanity lost in stormy confusion and we were the reaching out helpless shadows of his fading light. It was like trying to direct the events in a dream as we drove past him and on into San Francisco, the car moving like a reel of film, splicing and editing itself, taking us further away from him.

Blue Sky

The question: How could I do it?
The answer: I didn't give it a second thought because

somehow it seemed natural to me, the thing to do, and with no regrets.

He had worked on the puzzle for three days. It was a thousand pieces which were supposed to add up to some boats in a harbor and lots of blue sky above.

The blue sky turned out to be the problem.

Everything else went as it was destined to go hour after hour, piece after piece, the harbor and the boats appeared.

Finally, it came down to the blue sky.

There was a lot of blue sky with nothing in it except itself and to finish it took hundreds of pieces. My friend pondered them through a long slow evening.

They fiercely resisted taking shape. He finally gave up, saying, "There is nothing here except blue sky. There are no clouds or anything to help me. Just the same blue sky. I give up."

And he went to bed and a fitful night's sleep.

The next day he did not work on the puzzle.

It lay 80% completed on the dining room table. It was finished except for a couple hundred pieces of blue. Above the harbor filled with boats was a huge hole the color of the table. It looked strange. The sky should not be brown.

My friend cautiously avoided the puzzle.

It was as if the Hound of the Baskervilles was sitting there on the table. He didn't want anything to do with that dog.

Early in the evening he sat down in a rocking chair in the front room and looked into the dining room where the puzzle sat on the table, licking its paws.

"I give up," he said, finally, breaking a long silence. "I can't finish it. The blue sky is hopeless."

Without saying a word, I went and got the vacuum cleaner and plugged it in. He sat there watching me. He didn't say anything while I took a long nozzle and vacuumed the puzzle off the table. It disappeared piece by piece into the vacuum cleaner: harbor, boats and unfinished blue sky until it was gone, the table empty, not a piece remaining.

I unplugged the vacuum cleaner and took it away with the puzzle inside of it.

When I came back, he spoke for the first time since I had vacuumed up his puzzle.

"There was just too much blue sky," he said.

An Eye for Good Produce

Sometimes I am sloppy when I dial the telephone. I don't get the number right and have to redial but I always dial her number very carefully as if I am an accountant for a glass factory.

I have just dialed her number and I wait and it rings . . . and . . . it rings again.

A third ring follows . . .

And a fourth.

I am listening to her telephone ring very carefully as if I am listening to a complicated piece of classical music or a couple of interesting people talking about a technical problem.

I am listening so carefully that I can see her telephone on the small wooden table in her front room. There is a book beside the telephone. It is a novel.

. . . a seventh ring passes, an eighth ring follows . . . I have been listening so carefully to her telephone ring that I am now in her apartment, standing beside it in the dark room, listening to it ring.

She is not home. She's gone out. She's someplace else.

Then I get bored with the telephone and begin wandering around her apartment. I turn the lights on and look at things. I look at a painting on the wall that I like and her bed is made very neatly. I can almost see my reflection in it, but that was last year.

There's some unopened mail on the kitchen table: bills. That's one of her habits. She doesn't like to open her bills. She opens all the rest of her mail but leaves the bills on the kitchen table. They pile up. Sometimes she has people over to dinner with the bills still on the table.

I open the refrigerator and look inside. There's half a tuna casserole there and half a bottle of wine and a tomato there. It looks like a good tomato. She's very talented at selecting produce.

Her cat comes into the kitchen and looks at me. He's seen me many times. He's bored with me. He leaves the room.

Now what?

The telephone has rung over twenty times or so . . . at least. She's not home.

I hang up.

Gone Before
We Open Our Eyes

I had nothing else to do but float along on a tide of memories carrying me toward no particular shore. I was lying in bed. It was the afternoon of a day that I would never really be in.

There are days like that when you just aren't there.

. . . gone before we open our eyes.

I was thinking about a long-time-ago room and the objects in that room. I could remember five or six of them and part of the feeling in that room but there were other things that I couldn't remember.

I tried as hard as I could but they wouldn't come back to me. Finally, I gave up and made a vow. I was going to write down what I had remembered of the room and the feeling there and then wait a few months before looking at it again. At that time I would take my notes and try again to remember more things about that room and how it felt.

I thought it was an interesting thing to do lying there floating on shoreless memories.

So far so good, except for one thing: When I finally got out of bed in the late afternoon of a day that would never be, I forgot to write down the things I remembered about the room, and I even went so far as to totally forget about the room until today, a week later, and now I can remember nothing about the room.

Alas, once upon a time there was a room that I have forgotten.

Harem

He is almost invisible wandering around Tokyo, taking photographs of beautiful women. He is so nondescript looking in appearance and presence that it is not possible to describe him. He is one of those people that even when you are looking at him you are forgetting him so that the second he is out of your sight he is totally forgotten.

The beautiful women are never aware that he is taking their photograph or if they are aware of it they instantly forget it.

He has thousands of photographs of beautiful women. He develops them in his own darkroom and makes life-size prints. He has the prints hanging like clothes in his closet on thousands of hangers.

Whenever he feels lonely he just takes one of them out.

Montana Love

There was an article in the paper yesterday about a mother sitting on her teen-age son, so that the police couldn't arrest and take him away.

The boy committed a crime and then ran home to his mother with the police in what I guess they call hot pursuit. They were trying to handcuff him when his mother came into the room, saw what was happening to her son, and then sat down on him, so the police couldn't finish their arrest.

I can imagine the thoughts that went through the police officers' minds when this happened. I can see them trying to talk the mother off her son.

Nobody needs this kind of shit. When people say to you, "Have a nice day," they don't mean for this to happen.

Come on, lady, get up.

Come on, lady, get off.

The woman was arrested for obstructing justice, "allegedly" sitting on her son.

Cat Cantaloupe

We were eating cantaloupe and it wasn't very good. We should have let it ripen a little longer or maybe it never would have tasted good. Perhaps it was a cantaloupe doomed to fail from the very beginning but we will really never know because it didn't have a full chance to prove itself.

When my wife and I finished, feeling vaguely unsatisfied, we put our plates on the floor. I don't know why. We could just as easily have put them on the coffee table.

We have a new borrowed cat in the house. Because we don't spend the entire year here in Montana, we lure our neighbors' cats over with extravagant promises of cat delicacies and all-expense paid vacations to the Cat Ritz in Paris. We have a lot of mice. The cats never get to Paris. When we leave Montana for California, the cats go back to their original homes with unused passports.

Anyway, the new cat walked over to the cantaloupe rinds on the floor and began very carefully examining one of them. The cat gave the cantaloupe an exploring lick. Then the cat, who would never get to use its French, gave the rind a few more licks, but they were very much more familiar.

The cat started eating the cantaloupe. I had never seen a cat eat cantaloupe before. I tried to imagine what the cantaloupe tasted like to the cat. I cannot think of anything that a cat would normally eat that would taste like a cantaloupe.

We have to rule out mice, birds, gophers, insects, and eliminate such housecat foods as fish, chicken, milk and all the stuff that comes in cans, pouches and boxes.

What is left that would taste like cantaloupe to a cat?

I have not the slightest idea nor will I probably ever have but I know one thing for certain: I will never walk

[69]

into a grocery store and go to the pet food section and see a
can of cat cantaloupe on the shelf.

Al's Rose Harbor

Al went to sea for ten years and saved his money. He
wanted to buy a bar because he liked good times. He
bought the bar. It was called Al's Good Time Harbor. It
failed because it was in the wrong location and he didn't
know anything about the bar business and he wouldn't let
any of his friends pay for drinks.

When he owned the bar, he had a lot of friends. He
thought the next time they came back they would bring
paying customers with them and those paying customers
would bring other paying customers. The free drinks he
was buying for all his friends were a good form of advertising that would contribute toward his having a chain of Al's
Good Time Harbors all over the world.

There would be one in Hong Kong and Sydney and Rio
de Janeiro and Honolulu and Denver and Yokohama, and

even an Al's Good Time Harbor in Paris, France! serving Three Star food. He would visit them, keep track of what was going on, in his own private jet with his own private stewardess right off the centerfold of *Playboy* magazine. When somebody bought the next issue of *Playboy* and turned to the centerfold, it would be blank because the Playmate would be flying beside him, holding his hand.

Al now lives with his mother.

He keeps telling her that he's going to sea next month but it's been two years. He doesn't get out of the house much and there are no ships on the horizon. His mother has a back yard full of roses. She likes roses. He doesn't because the red ones are too red and the yellow ones are too yellow and the pink ones are too pink.

Sometimes he stares out his bedroom window at the roses, wondering why that is and wishing that roses were more inbetween.

Farewell to the First Grade
and Hello
to the *National Enquirer*

I always had trouble with school, especially the first grade. I became the tallest kid in the first grade by flunking it a couple of times. I just could not figure out how the first grade worked. I started off in the first grade as an average-size kid and a couple of years later I was the tallest kid in the first grade.

Reading was a particular problem for me. It did not make any sense at all. For the first couple of years that I spent in the first grade I might as well have read the books upside down for all it got me.

Eventually I taught myself to read because after a few years in the first grade it got pretty nerve-racking and the tedium approached a kind of blank religious experience, while I sat there busy growing away from September until June when I was paroled for a few months from the first grade before returning to it again in the fall.

I taught myself to read by figuring out what store signs and food products were saying. I would walk very slowly down the street and puzzle out SAM'S SHOE REPAIR, GOOD FOOD CAFE, AL'S SMOKE SHOP, FAST AND CLEAN LAUNDRY, NEON WAFFLE SHOP, ECONOMY MARKET, MABLE'S BEAUTY COLLEGE, and the ANTLER TAVERN where there were a lot of antlers in the front window and a lot more antlers inside.

People would sit around and drink beer and look at all the antlers while outside I studied menus in restaurant windows and slowly came to understand what the words steak, mashed potatoes, hamburger, salad and butter meant.

Sometimes I would go to a grocery store to study English. I would walk up and down the aisles reading the labels off cans. There were pictures on the cans which helped a lot. I would look at the picture of some peas on a can and read the word peas and put it together. I would hang around the canned fruit section and learn peaches, cherries, plums, pears, oranges and pineapple. I learned my fruits very quickly after I had made the big decision that I wanted out of the first grade.

The most difficulty I had in learning my fruits was of course fruit cocktail.

Sometimes I would just stand there holding a can in my

[73]

hands, staring at it for ten or fifteen minutes, getting no closer to the truth.

That was thirty-seven years ago and my reading habits since then have bobbed up and down like a cork on a roller coaster horizon. Right now one of my favorite things to read is the *National Enquirer*. I am a real fan. I like stories about people and there are a lot of stories about people in the *National Enquirer*. This week's *Enquirer* had articles with titles like these:

Food Causes Most Marriage Problems,
Short People Live Longer,
We Were Taken to a Mysterious City in an Alien World,
Why President Truman Always Washed His Own
    Underwear,
Angry Drivers Using Cars as Deadly Weapons,
"Lois Lane" Fumes Over Topless Photo,
Professors Wasting Your Tax $$ to Study Crickets.

I started reading the *National Enquirer* by originally reading the Sunday *New York Times* while I watched television. It was actually quite simple: One day I just substituted the *National Enquirer* for *The New York Times*, and that was that.

I let somebody else buy my copy of *The New York Times* instead of me. They could have my copy and the responsibility for being a thinking and aware person. I am forty-four years old and thank God, I got out of the first grade and sometimes all I want to do is have a little mindless fun with the years that are left in my life.

[74]

I am happy as a clam reading the *National Enquirer* while watching television.

The Wolf Is Dead

I have waited years for him to die, for death to come like an erasing wind and take him away with it and all the things that he stood for, which somehow have come to me to be symbolic of the 1970s.

His life for most of the decade was an uninterrupted pattern of pacing back and forth in a cage beside the highway. I never saw him standing still. He was always moving. His future was only his next step.

I first saw him in 1972 when I came back to Montana after an absence of thirty years and I would see him every year after that, always doing the same thing, pacing, until this autumn of 1978. I was gone from Montana for six months and when I came back he was gone. We had changed places.

The wolf must have died during the summer. There

[75]

were grass and weeds growing in his empty cage when I came back. While he was alive, which was the 1970s, nothing grew there because of his endless walking. He walked the decade away a step at a time. If all those steps were put together, he probably walked halfway to the moon.

I am glad he is dead because I don't think a wolf should spend his life in a cage by the highway, but I don't want you to think that the wolf was on public exhibition. He was somebody's private pet and the cage was beside that person's house.

The owner's position probably went something like this, "I have a wolf for a pet," and whatever would happen then, would happen after that.

But the wolf is dead now.

Weeds grow in his cage.

His journey to the moon is over.

The Closest I Have Been
to the Sea Since Evolution

Last weekend staying on the Japanese coast with friends,
I had fish for every meal, fish for breakfast, lunch and dinner. I even had fish for a bedtime snack. I had raw fish,
dried fish, broiled fish and just fish fish.

I must have eaten twenty different kinds of fish and they
were all delicious, but after a while I literally had fish
coming out of *my* gills.

One morning I took a shit and it smelled just like the
sea. There was no difference between the smell of my shit
and walking along a beach or sitting on a wharf, staring at
ships and the sun going down behind them into billions of
years of water.

After that shit I understood a little more about my roots
that once swam with fish and my first home under the sea
where I grew slowly like a garden toward the land.

[77]

Homage to Groucho Marx

1890 – 1977

"Locomotives!" he yelled.

He wanted a definite answer.

In fact: He demanded it.

"Locomotives!" he yelled again, and then waited impatiently for my reply. I very carefully chose my words as if I were a jeweler cutting a diamond in swiftly moving fog. I wanted them to have a lot to do with his life, so much so that he wouldn't be able to understand them.

I thought that was the least I could do for him, seeing that he was so interested in my response and had come such a long distance to get it. I'm not saying that he had travelled around the world for it, but I'm not excluding that as a possibility.

He did look tired.

I would have offered him a doughnut if I'd had one.

[78]

Of course he was young but he was not as young as he would have you believe. He was one of those men who are thirty-one and constantly refer to themselves in the third person as "the kid" and make excuses to total strangers for mistakes that they have made, blaming it on a lack of experience, being young.

Sometimes they don't even make the mistakes in front of you. They only make the excuses without having done anything.

In other words: They want you to treat them as if they are fourteen years old . . . sweet, unending fourteen.

I slowly began answering his question by changing the subject from a curious question about locomotives to reminiscing about a few days I spent years ago in Connecticut.

I stayed with some people that I didn't know. Nothing much happened except that the meals were very, very long and often served outside on a patio that didn't have a roof and as I remember it rained all the time that I was there.

I never knew that it could take so long to eat a hamburger.

I was uncomfortable staying there and I think the people were uncomfortable having me. The last morning I had breakfast with them they didn't give me an umbrella.

After I left I never got in touch with them again. It was a chance and accidental meeting that brought us together in the first place. I think that we were all much better off apart.

When I was packing to leave their house I forgot a

sweater that was hanging in the closet. I didn't find out about it until later when I arrived home the next day after a long bus trip. I knew that they would never write to me about finding the sweater.

And they never did.

It was a cheerful sacrifice on my part.

The idea of having anything more to do with those people was entirely out of the question. It wasn't even within a stone's throw of the answer.

"So be the sweater," I said, earnestly to the "kid" finishing my reply.

He stared at me in total disbelief as if an elephant had stepped into the shower with him. "I wasn't talking about a sweater," he said. "I was asking you a question about locomotives. Where did the sweater come from?"

"Forget it," I said. "It's gone now."

A Feeling of Helplessness

There's not enough work for the waitresses. They need more customers in the restaurant. The waitresses have gathered at the back of the restaurant where I am sitting alone at a table. They are just standing around. They are awkward, impatient. There are five of them. They are all middle-aged and wearing white shoes, black skirts and white blouses.

They need more customers.

I take another bite of chicken fried steak. Three waitresses are absentmindedly staring at me. I pile up some corn on my fork. Perhaps they want to remember what a customer looks like. I take a sip of ice water. Now there are four waitresses staring at me.

The fifth waitress is looking at the front door. She wants it to open and a party of four people to come in and sit down at one of her tables. But she'll settle for a sixty-year-old woman who just wants a cup of coffee and a piece of pie.

I return to another bite of chicken fried steak. The fifth waitress joins the other four waitresses in staring at me but I've done all I can to help. There's nothing more that I can do. If only I could eat five chicken fried steaks at five different tables, my life would be much simpler.

One Arm Burning in Tokyo

All I know about him is that he was twenty years old and he jumped out the 6th floor window of his hospital room.

In the overwhelming rush of America like a self-devouring roller coaster and our problems of life and death everywhere all around us, 24 hours a day, never stopping, our friends and families, total strangers, even the President of the United States, his friends and everybody that they know, I take time out today to think about the suicide of a young Japanese boy.

I didn't read about it in the newspaper or see it on television. A friend told me about it while explaining why a young man working for her did not come to work yesterday. He was good friends with the boy who committed suicide and went to the funeral and was too disturbed afterwards to work.

My friend said that the dead boy had been in an automobile accident and had lost his arm. Overwhelmed by the shock of losing his arm, he jumped out the window of his hospital room.

First, he lost his arm in an automobile accident and then grieving for his lost arm, he took his own life. He didn't want the rest of his years: to fall in love, marriage, children, a career, middle age, old age and then death with only one arm.

He didn't want any of that, so he jumped out the window of his hospital room.

When my friend told me the story, she said, "It was a big waste. Why did he have to do that? A man can learn to live with one arm."

Well, he couldn't, and the end was just the same, anyway: A one-armed corpse burning in a crematorium. Where the other arm should have been burning, there was nothing.

Rubber Bands

. . . sixty and a few more scattered down the sidewalk for ¾'s of a block or so . . . They attracted my sleepy reptilian attention which has been like a snake left out too long in the sun recently. I haven't been feeling very good. A spell of middle age and poor health have been grinding me down.

Most of the rubber bands were in a thirty-foot place and the rest journeyed sporadically on their way to wherever rubber bands go when they are tossed out in the street.

I stopped and looked at the rubber bands. They looked OK to me. I wondered why the person who dropped them didn't bother to pick them up. Maybe there were a lot more where they came from. Maybe the person didn't care very much about rubber bands to begin with. Maybe the person hated rubber bands and this was a long planned revenge.

Suddenly, I was aware that I was standing there in the street thinking about rubber bands. I don't know how much time had passed. I have better things to do than think about rubber bands. What about my eternal soul and its day to day battle with the powers of good and evil? And besides, I have plenty of my own rubber bands. I have a whole box full on my desk. They are enough.

I don't need these lost, abandoned rubber bands. If you want to play, you have to pay. Let them take care of their own fate. I walked away from the rubber bands, feeling somehow vindicated as if I could make it through another twenty-four hours.

This morning when I went down to get a cup of coffee at a small café, the rubber bands were still there, but I didn't care.

Werewolf Raspberries

(*with a Glenn Miller record playing in the background, perhaps "Tuxedo Junction"*)

. . . and all you wanted to do was take your best girl out into the garden on a full moon night and give her a great big kiss . . . too bad the raspberries were covered with fur and you couldn't see their little teeth shining in the moonlight. Things might have been different.

If you had played your cards right, you could have been killed at Pearl Harbor instead.

Late spring
1940

Toothbrush Ghost Story

This little story illustrates the sensitivity of Japanese women. It is about a toothbrush and of course there is always the chance that it is not true, that it is just a story somebody made up and if that's the case, I am sorry I have wasted your time but we will never know if this story is true or not, will we?

Once upon a time in Tokyo a young American man and a young Japanese woman met and one thing led to another, like lust, and they became lovers, but she was much more serious about their affair than he was. By this time, a month or so had passed and she had spent many nights at his apartment, leaving in the morning to go home or to work.

One night she brought her toothbrush with her. She had always used his toothbrush before. She asked if she could leave her toothbrush there. Because she was spending so many nights there, she might as well use her toothbrush instead of his all the time. He said yes and she put her toothbrush beside his in the toothbrush holder. They made love as they usually did, shining brightly with the health of youthful lust. The next morning she happily brushed her teeth with her own toothbrush and went off to her day.

After she was gone, he thought about their love affair. He liked her but not nearly as much as she liked him. He thought about her bringing her toothbrush to his apartment. He went into the bathroom and looked at it. The sight of her toothbrush beside his did not please him. Things were starting to get out of control.

He took her toothbrush out of the holder and put it in the garbage. Later that day he stopped at a drugstore and bought the cheapest toothbrush that you can buy in Japan. Her toothbrush had been blue. This one was red. He put it beside his toothbrush in the bathroom where hers had been.

That evening she came to visit him.

They had a drink and talked for a while.

She was feeling very comfortable.

Then she had to go to the bathroom.

[87]

She was gone for ten minutes.

She took more time than she should have taken. He waited. He carefully took a sip of whiskey. He held it in his mouth for a while before he swallowed it. Then he waited.

She came out of the bathroom.

When she went into the bathroom she had been very happy and relaxed. When she came out of the bathroom, she was very quiet and composed. She told him she had forgotten about an appointment she had made that night, and that it was a very important business meeting and she was very sorry but she had to leave immediately. He said that he understood and she thanked him for understanding.

He never saw her again.

Skylab at the Graves
of Abbott and Costello

Every time I look at the chickens these days here in Montana, north of Yellowstone National Park, I think about something and finally it's reached the point where I have to share it with another person, so for better or for worse, here it is.

Oh, yes, a word of warning:

If you are expecting something dramatic to be revealed about chickens and their place in the firmament, forget about it. What I am about to reveal here could not be used as the plot for a disaster movie starring Burt Reynolds as a chicken rancher who takes the law in his own hands with brilliant cameo appearances by Reggie Jackson, Lillian Carter, Red Buttons, Bill Walton, Elizabeth Taylor, the graves of Abbott and Costello, and also starring Charlton Heston as "Oak."

[89]

Last week I was taking some leftover ears of corn out to the chickens. I like to liven up their lives with scraps, so they will be stimulated to lay inspired eggs, eggs that are just like going to church.

When the chickens saw me leave the house carrying something toward them, they all ran over to the fence and waited for me. My appearances at the chicken house with leftover goodies from the kitchen constitute a large part of their day.

Sometimes I feel like chorale director because the chickens are always making a big racket clucking away as I start toward them. I wonder how *The Messiah* would sound sung by eighteen chickens.

I was carrying six very large ears of corn in a small plastic bag, but if you really want the truth: The ears of corn were actually huge, gigantic, larger than life!

I planned on just dumping them over the fence and going on with the rest of my life. When I got to the chicken yard and saw the chickens all gathered closely together, I realized that I had better be careful because I didn't want to dump the ears of corn on the chickens' heads. I had a vision of three or four chickens being knocked cold by huge ears of corn falling from the sky. I didn't like that idea at all.

I could see them lying unconscious with the other chickens gathered solemnly around their fallen comrades and looking up at me with expressions of anti-imperialistic hatred in their eyes:

"YANKEE DOG, GO HOME!"

No, no, I didn't want nor need that responsibility piled on a life that already had enough problems, so I took a few steps down the fence away from the chickens and shook the corn out of the bag.

As the ears of corn fell en masse out of the plastic bag, one chicken rushed out of the flock toward me and all six ears landed right on his head. They of course did not knock him unconscious. They caused him to be knocked sideways and then jump a foot in the air. Then down he came, gave his head a good shake to make sure that it was still there and joined in eating with the other chickens who did not give a damn about six ears of corn landing on this dumbbell's head.

I went away a little confused myself and thinking about the possibilities of six ears of corn and eighteen possible chicken head targets and how that one chicken got all the corn on his head. There should have been other combinations. For instance: One ear of corn on six different chicken heads or two ears of corn on one chicken head and three ears of corn on single chicken heads and the remaining ear of corn missing altogether a possible chicken head and just falling harmlessly on the ground.

I think you get the picture of what was going on in my mind except that I have not told you the reason for this story. Sometimes I feel just like the chicken who got all six ears of corn on his head.

The Bed Salesman

He sits alone in a sea of beds. They break around him
like silent, motionless waves. It is a rainy winter day in
San Francisco and nobody wants to buy a bed. He is a
middle-aged man and very bored. He sits there surrounded
by beds of every flavor and variety. There are maybe fifty
or sixty double beds in the huge showroom and he is sitting on one of them.

He realizes that the situation is hopeless because he has
taken his suit coat off and is just sitting there. He is wearing a dress shirt with a tie but he should have his coat on
to create a responsible appearance, somebody who sin-
cerely wants to sell beds, but he just doesn't give a damn
right now.

"Nobody is going to buy a bed today," he thinks. "I
might as well be comfortable."

He also knows that his boss would not approve of him
taking his coat off, but his boss is at the dentist having a

wisdom tooth extracted, so . . . that takes care of the boss.

Rain continues to fall.

It will come down all day long.

He stares out at the rain through the huge panoramic windows of the bed store but he doesn't see it. For a few seconds he thinks about how he got into selling beds for a living. He took pre-med in college with the dream of being a doctor but he doesn't complete the thought. It's too depressing to finish, so his mind just blanks out.

Meanwhile, the beds wait for owners.

They wait for the stillness of sleepers and the spring-disturbing antics of passion makers. They wait for the thousands of clean sheets that will become dirty sheets. It will all begin very simply with two virginal sheets.

People will be created and people will die in these beds.

The beds wait to be in museums centuries from now, providing wonder and amusement for people wearing strange clothes and perhaps speaking languages that have not been invented yet.

The salesman, almost lost in an immensity of beds, does not know that he is a shepherd of the future and these beds are his flock.

Tire Chain Bridge

The 1960s:

A lot of people remember hating President Lyndon Baines Johnson and loving Janis Joplin and Jim Morrison, depending on the point of view. God rest their souls.

I remember an Indian woman looking for a tire chain in the snow. She was about fifty or so and we didn't see her at first. It was New Mexico 1969. We saw her brother standing patiently beside a blue Age-of-Aquarius pickup truck parked on the side of the road. He was about her age, but as I said just a few words ago, she wasn't there. We wouldn't see her until later.

Because he was basically parked in the middle of nowhere we stopped and asked him if he needed any help.

"No," he said. "Everything's just fine."

That being settled we asked if we could get through on the road to the obscure place where we were headed: some old Indian ruins. I might add all this is taking place in a snowy landscape and the other person that it took to make a we or an us was a long since gone girlfriend. The last I heard she was in South America.

Jeeping it in New Mexico, we were just driving around in the late winter, early spring, taking in the sights with not many people to distract us.

"The road's good," the Indian said. "There's more snow here than there is ahead. It's pretty good three or four miles from here. This is the worst."

That made us feel better.

The road was a white tire track vagueness that disappeared into a premature horizon. There were fat beaconesque mesas towering up from the desert floor. The road vanished somewhere in between their shipless vigilance.

I had a strong feeling that the mesas didn't give a damn about that road. To them the road was just a passing cartoon. After all, they had been witnesses to the beginning of time.

"My sister's out there," the Indian said, casually pointing down the road that very shortly vanished off the face of the earth.

"What?" I said, not quite hearing or maybe just not believing what he had just said.

"She's looking for the chain. I lost a tire chain out there. She's looking for it."

I looked down the road.

I didn't see anybody.

"About a mile or so," he said, still pointing.

He had one foot on the running board of the pickup.

[95]

"There's somebody out there," I said, still playing straight man.

"My sister," he said. "I hope she finds that chain. It cost me three dollars. Used."

"Yeah," I said, blindly. What else could I say because I certainly couldn't see an Indian woman down that road looking for a three-dollar tire chain?

"When you see her," he said, "tell her I'm still here waiting."

"OK," I said, my voice like a white cane tapping along.

We said our good-byes and continued down the road for a mile or so, and like the Indian said, we saw her walking along the side of the road looking in the snow for the tire chain.

She was looking very carefully for it in the late-cold, snowy-clear New Mexico morning. We stopped beside her and she looked up from her tire chain searching. Her face was weathered with patience, her eyes echoed timelessness.

I think the Queen of England would be impatient by now if she had been looking for a three-dollar tire chain in the snow.

"Your brother's waiting for you," I said, like a blindman, motioning with my head down the road.

"I know," she said. "He's good at that."

"Any luck?" I said, like a bat.

I could see that she wasn't carrying the tire chain, so obviously she hadn't found it, but I had to say something.

"It's here someplace," she said, glancing with her eyes

[96]

at the nearby 121,000 square miles, which is the area of New Mexico.

"Good luck," I said, ten years ago in the Sixties that have become legend now like the days of King Arthur sitting at the Round Table with the Beatles, and John singing "Lucy in the Sky with Diamonds."

We drove down the road toward the Seventies, leaving her slowly behind, looking for a tire chain in the snow with her brother waiting patiently beside a blue pickup truck with its Age-of-Aquarius paint job starting to flake.

White

Whenever I seriously think about the color white, I think about her, for she is the ultimate definition of white.

She was at a combination exhibition of paintings and autograph party for a famous Japanese painter-writer. She was very interested in him as he sat at a table autographing copies of his latest book. There was a long line of people waiting for his autograph. She did not get in line but wandered around and around and around the gallery, looking but not looking at his paintings.

She was very beautiful with an incredible pair of legs that she showed off like an event, which they were. She crowned them with a pair of black, almost shark-like high heel shoes.

The woman knew how to provoke attention.

From time to time she walked near the table where the writer was autographing away like some king of machine. He autographed books as if Sony had invented him.

He never noticed her.

She had a way of walking very slowly seven or eight premeditated steps and then turning swiftly on her heel like a shark turning to attack.

As the hours passed, the line of people gradually evaporated down to just a handful and then she walked dramatically as if a spotlight were on her to the table. She took a copy of his book out of her purse and waited for the people that were in front of her to disappear off the earth.

Then it was her turn.

I can imagine the sound of her heart as she stood there waiting. The writer took the book and signed it without looking up. That was all. She turned very slowly and walked away. She never looked back, going out the door.

She was wearing a white dress.

Montana Traffic Spell

We all have moments in life when we don't know what to do next. Here is one of them: A friend and I were driving down the Mainstreet of a small town in Montana. It was a cloudy autumn late-afternoon and we came to a green light. It was the only traffic light in town: the shepherd of a sleepy intersection.

My friend wanted to turn right on the light but he hesitated for no apparent reason except that suddenly he didn't know what to do next.

My friend is an experienced driver, so it had nothing to do with his driving ability. He just didn't know what to do next and I sat there watching him with a great deal of interest, wondering how it was all going to turn out.

We weren't moving on the green light and suddenly there was a line of cars building up behind us. I don't know where they had come from in such a small town but they were now behind us. For some strange reason nobody was making a fuss, not even honking a horn, over us completely stopping the traffic.

We were just a long line of cars stopping for no reason at a green light. Perhaps, they didn't know what to do next either.

We were all in a cloudy Montana approaching-twilight spell, just sitting there in our cars, some of us patiently listening to the radio, others anxious to get home to family and loved ones or just to go someplace by yourself and do something that was your own business, but nothing was happening. We were at a complete standstill.

I don't know how long this went on.

It could have been thirty seconds or a year might have passed taking us in a full circle right back to where we had started from.

There was no way of knowing.

We were all helpless.

We didn't know what to do next.

Then a man in the car right behind us solved the problem. It was so easy that I don't know why it wasn't done before. It changed everything and we made the right turn and all the other cars drove on past us committed now to finish their destinations.

Nobody knew what to do next until the man behind us rolled his car window down and yelled at the top of his lungs: "MOVE, YOU SON-OF-A-BITCH!"

That took care of it.

Hangover as Folk Art

For Jim Harrison

Yesterday I had a hangover here in Tokyo that was so painful and exhausting that I could only think of it as grotesque folk art. It was being sold by vendors that you don't want to know about.

Normally, a real bad hangover bites the dust when the sun goes down. It dies like a snake. This hangover didn't die at all. It changed into folk art made from my central nervous system, my stomach and the little stretches of imagination I call my brain.

The folk art took the shapes of badly carved, smelly little dolls, undesirable tainted trinkets constructed from rusty beer cans and coal, paintings of alligator shit on swamp bark, and of course, last but not least, colorful native shirts woven out of the underwear removed from corpses by albino grave robbers who can only rob graves on full moon

[101]

nights. They work at the most twelve nights a year and the rest of the time it's unemployment for them. They stay around the house and watch a lot of television. During the commercials they beat their wives.

In other words: I simply don't want a day like yesterday again in my life. When the hangover finally ended, the folk art vendors had vanished, taking their strange and dubious wares with them. They also took every feeling in my body with them except for an abstract chalky awareness that I was still breathing.

Right, Jim?

Marching in the
Opposite Direction of a Pizza

They are like a strange army returning from the front for a brief rest before going back into battle again here in Tokyo. Four of them just came by in uniform which consists of blue pants and red and white striped shirts. They were not wearing their helmets that look like plastic straw hats. Their military discipline is relaxed because they are on what the army calls furlough. They are on furlough from making pizzas. Just a short distance away is a Shakey's Pizza Parlor. These crack troops are young Japanese men who make pizzas there. They are on break or furlough from a battlefield whose lines, yards won and lost, are measured in pizzas eaten.

As they walk by, I know one thing for certain in this world and it may be the only thing I do know, they are not going to get a pizza.

Dogs on the Roof

I could see the dogs standing on the roof from a long distance away. There were two of them: collies (quite small), but as I bicycled toward them they grew larger and larger until eventually they would start barking when I was close enough.

There was a small polluted creek beside the house and a

small tangled woods behind the house. It was a very dense and unfriendly woods, the kind that scratches you and tears your clothes.

The house itself wasn't much to look at. It was two stories high and wooden: hard to describe and easy to forget except for the dogs on the roof.

Often I had to bicycle past that house.

I don't know how the dogs got onto the roof but they were there.

Once they didn't bark at me and that made me nervous. Hard as it is to believe, their barking was easier to take than their silence.

They just stood there on the roof staring at me as I bicycled past.

I never once saw the people that lived in the house.

I hope the dogs didn't live there alone.

California Mailman

Until recently, I've never been a very intuitive person and my ESP temperature has always hovered in the low zeroes like 27 below. But all that changed a few months ago when I had a dream that came true. It is the first time this ever happened to me. I dreamt that my mail would be very boring and uninteresting in the months to come and that's the way it's been since the dream.

All I get are bills and junkmail and trivia.

When I see the mailman coming up the walk, my eyelids slowly lower. Sometimes I fall asleep while I am opening an envelope.

California is ready for anything.

I wonder if I should start a cult.

The Cobweb Toy

I remember five years ago when he first became famous. It was a beautiful toy and he had a lot of fun with it. I enjoyed watching his pleasure. He is a very good writer and deserved the fame.

Now: He has published a book about the Acid Shadow of Fame that eats at the heart and soul until ambiguity and disarray are as predictable as the time the sun rises and the sun goes down.

Today the sun came up at 6:13 a.m. and went down at 6:22 p.m.

It was only five years ago.

My, how time flies.

Her Last Known Boyfriend
a Canadian Airman

Her last known boyfriend was a Canadian airman who was shot down over Germany in November 1944. Their romance only lasted a week and they never went to bed together. They were going to get married after the war.

He was twenty-two and she was nineteen.

They met by accident at a bus stop in San Francisco. He had never talked to a Chinese woman before. She was the only other person waiting for a bus. He was a very cheerful and outward going young man. People instantly liked him.

[106]

"Hello," he said. "I'm from Canada."

They wrote every day after he was gone, promising each other the future. They were going to have three children: two boys and a girl.

The last letter she got was written by an air force chaplain:

He often spoke of you, etc.

He asked me to write to you if, etc.

I know that he would want you to, etc.

When she finished reading the letter, her life was over and she had joined him in death. She quit college where she was a straight-A student and got a job washing dishes in a Chinese restaurant on Jackson Street. People working at the restaurant thought it very strange and disturbing that a beautiful young woman should be washing dishes for a living.

There were so many other things that she could have done.

She was like a ghost in the kitchen.

Over the years they would try to talk to her about it but she didn't say anything and they always gave up. Finally, no one cared any more because she was no longer beautiful.

The only thing that was known about her was that she had once been in love with a Canadian airman.

She never looks up from the dishes.

Thirty-four years . . .

She scrapes the remains of uneaten food off the plates of people that she never sees. Their eating is the cemetery where she is buried.

The Butcher

You can't cut meat when you're wearing gloves and nobody wants to buy meat from somebody wearing them either. Gloves and meat do not go hand in hand. That's why the butcher has cold hands. I know because he told me so.

I was in a San Francisco meat market, thinking about having some meat for dinner. I didn't know what kind. I paced up and down the meat counter. I walked past pork chops, hamburger, lamb shanks, dead chickens, and fresh but dusty-eyed fish.

The butcher watched me without saying anything and he didn't move either. There was a kind of forlorn expression on his middle-aged face that had gone as far in life as it was going to go. Now it would become the face of an old man.

I stopped and stared at a piece of round steak. It did not catch my fancy and I walked back toward a lamb chop that was a little more interesting. I stood there staring at one chop in the middle of twenty-five other chops. It was on top of the other chops and looked as if it had climbed up there. I admired its spunk.

The other twenty-four chops did nothing for me. They might as well have been nameless sand. I thought about applying heat to that chop and eating it for dinner. I was living by myself, so that chop would grace a solitary meal.

It was a dreary day in San Francisco, overcast and futureless like it gets sometimes in the summer and can stay that way for days. You begin to wonder if there is any summer at all going on in America.

"I have cold hands," the butcher said.

I looked up from the chop.

I didn't know who he was talking to.

He was talking to me.

I looked at his hands.

He was holding them despairingly out in front of him. They were a used-up sort of gray and red. Those hands had been cold for years leading into decades of dead meat.

I tried to think of a proper response. My hands were suddenly very warm, actually hot. I felt very guilty. My tongue was deserty and I was lost without water in that desert.

The butcher broke the chains of my predicament by saying, "I could have been a truck driver. I drove a truck in the Army. I guess that's what I should have done. At least, my hands wouldn't be cold all the time."

By this time, the blood in my hands was boiling.

I forced a kind of half-smile that people try to pretend

means that they understand and sympathize with when
somebody says something that there is no good way to
respond to.

The butcher rubbed his hands together and tried to
break the tension by telling a little joke, but not a single
word came out of him. His mouth started to move but
then it stopped and we both smiled as if he had actually
told the joke.

As he walked toward me and my lamb chop, he was still
rubbing his hands together.

To the Yotsuya Station

By any standard she would be considered a good-looking
woman and maybe in her early thirties. She has fine fea-
tures, a perfect little mouth that looks as if it had been
built by roses working overtime in a rare factory. The only
flaw in her face is her eyes. They are beautiful eyes but
lack a certain character that's not important because most

men aren't particularly interested in a woman's character, anyway.

Her body is nice to look at, compact and well-proportioned. She has trim ankles and a bust that stops just short of being generous.

As we hurtle along on the subway underneath Tokyo, she sits across from me, absentmindedly playing with the skin under her chin. She pulls gently on it, checking out its firmness again and again as we stop at a station and then hurtle forward to the next station.

Above us twelve million people are trying to be happy and make the best of their lives while she continues to think about the firmness of her chin and the years to come, which will certainly come. They will come just like the station in front of us that we are hurtling toward.

Welcome to the Yotsuya Station.

It's just another stop on the way.

A Safe Journey Like This River

Above all these
things
put on charity . . .
—Col. 3:14

Last night there was a knock at the kitchen door of this ranch house in Southern Montana, near the banks of the Yellowstone River on its way to join up with the Missouri River, then onto the Mississippi River travelling down to the Gulf of Mexico, its eventual home, so far away from these mountains, this kitchen door and the knocking of last night.

I was busy cooking something. I couldn't quite believe that somebody was knocking at the kitchen door. A friend talking to me in the kitchen answered it before I could move. I had been paying close attention to a frying pan full of chicken and mushrooms.

I waited for the people to come into the kitchen and see who they were and what they wanted. I also wondered why they hadn't come to the front door. It's easier to get to, at the front of the house, so to speak. It's right on the way. I don't remember anybody ever coming around to the kitchen door at night. Maybe somebody did once, a long time ago, but I wasn't living here, then.

The people didn't come into the kitchen. They just stood outside on the back porch talking to my friend for the briefest of times and then my friend closed the door and the people were gone without my having seen them.

The few words they said sounded like children talking: "Welcome to Paradise Valley."

That's all I could make out.

My friend stood there with a small yellow pamphlet in his hands.

"Who was that?" I said.

"Two girls inviting us to church."

The handmade yellow pamphlet was about the churches here in the valley:

Paradise Valley Community Church
Pine Creek Methodist Church
St. John's Episcopal Church
Emigrant, Mont.

It was a simple and cheerfully mimeographed pamphlet listing the names of the ministers, their telephone numbers and the various types and times of worship offered at the churches.

[113]

There was a decal of flowers pasted on the yellow cover and a nice quote from Colossians to keep it company.

My friend told me the girls were ten or eleven years old. I never saw them but it was nice of them to come by one autumn evening and invite us to church. They have good hearts. I wish the best in life for them and a safe journey like the Yellowstone River flowing to the Gulf of Mexico, its faraway home and future.

These children will also flow away.

Parking Place Lost

It's a hot day and a young priest steps out of a church door, almost bumping into me. He is wearing a black, short-sleeve shirt. Maybe some kind of priest summerwear? I don't know but it is a warm day.

"It's gone!" the priest says, glancing angrily at some cars parked in front of the church. The cars occupy all the parking places. He stamps his foot on the sidewalk like a gravely-dressed little kid.

He shakes his head in disgust.

"It was here just a minute ago!" he says. "Now we'll have to find another place to park." He is talking to an older priest who walked out just after him and says nothing.

I hope there is plenty of parking in Paradise.

Studio 54

Ever time: and I am talking about a period of seven years, I call a certain friend on the telephone, he is always home. I've called him maybe sixty or seventy times during these seven years and he always answers.

There is no intentional pattern to my calling. It is strictly random dialing. I just call him when I feel like it. My finger pokes seven holes in the telephone and his voice automatically returns, "Hello."

Most of the time our conversations are not important, but what is important is that he is always there. Sometimes it is in the morning and sometimes it is at night.

He says he has a job, but what proof do I have? He says he got married a few years ago, but I have never met his wife and she never answers the phone.

I called him today at 1:15 in the afternoon and of course he was there. The phone rang only once. Lately, I've been thinking that since 1972 he has just been sitting around, waiting for me to call.

Crows Eating a Truck Tire in the Dead of Winter

We left Pine Creek, Montana, and headed down the road toward Bozeman to pick up a friend at the airport. He was flying in from Los Angeles, California.

The snow was very deep, locking up the ground like a white jail, and the temperature was a permanent 13 below zero with a meat ax wind showing who was boss of the North Country.

My friend was going to have quite a surprise when he

[116]

landed. The expression on his face would be interesting to observe. The palm trees that he drove by on his way to Los Angeles International Airport only a few hours ago would instantly become a distant part of the past when he got out of that airplane. Those trees could have been in his childhood. Maybe he saw them when he was six years old.

I was right and we drove back to Pine Creek.

The road was an icy sword cutting starkly through country that wore winter like a suit of albino armor.

We went around a bend in the road and there were six huge crows black as a blindman's dreams. The crows were eating a truck tire in the center of the road. They didn't move as we approached them. They didn't show any fear or a desire to let us pass. They just kept eating the truck tire. We drove around them.

"You've got some winter here," my friend said, LA gone, now only a ghost town in his mind. "Those crows are hungry."

[117]

Something Cooking

I've been thinking about this for years. It's been like a soup simmering on the back burner of my mind. I've stirred the soup thousands of time . . . often out of nervousness as the years have slipped away, leaving me older and older, and not quite the man I once was.

. . . of course it has to be a woman . . . that's taken so much time . . . cooking

slowly down

until finally I have arrived at these words: I don't know her name or what she looked like other than she was a short blond woman, and comely. I think she had blue eyes but I'll never be certain.

I do remember that she had a very healthy outlook on things and glowed with cheerfulness, though I can remember only one thing we talked about.

I was very drunk. Whiskey had obscured my intelligence

[118]

like a tropical rainstorm. Soaking wet monkeys were at play in my mind.

But she was interested in me, though what I was saying could hardly have made any sense. I remember her looking up at me. She was amused. We talked for a few moments or was it hours? We were in a bar someplace. There were a lot of people. They were a shimmering have of clothing.

She kept listening to me.

The one thing I remember talking to her about was her body.

I wanted it.

"Yes!" she said, very enthusiastically—"But come back when you're sober."

That's the only thing I remember her saying the next morning, which was years ago, when I woke up alone in bed with a classic hangover like feeding time in an anteater grotto and you're it, buster. I still had my clothes on or perhaps more accurately yet, my clothes had me on . . . oh, God! I couldn't remember where I had been or how I got home.

So I lay there hurting and thinking about her.

I took her words, like fresh ingredients, and carefully sliced them into a huge mental pot, along with everything else about her that I had said here, and put a slow fire under the pot because it would have to cook for years.

"Yes!" she said, very enthusiastically—"But come back when you're sober."

Too bad I didn't know where back was.

[119]

Cold Kingdom Enterprise

Once upon a time there was a dwarf knight who only had fifty word to live in and they were so fleeting that he only had time to put on a suit of armor and ride swiftly on a black horse into a very well-lit woods where he vanished forever.

The Beautiful Oranges of Osaka

Osaka is a Southern Japanese heavy industrial area of 8,333,845 people. It is not known for oranges.

This evening I was thinking about eating beautiful oranges from Osaka. They were so sweet, so delicious, so orangy. I could see them growing in thousands of orchards all around Osaka which was known as the Orange Capital of the Orient.

I could see the city almost possessed by oranges. Everybody eating oranges, talking about oranges and oranges on every tongue. Oranges and more oranges, and the babies of Osaka smelled like orange blossoms. I am also the only person who ever thought about this.

Drowned Japanese Boy

Somebody has to take his tennis shoes off. As an after-
thought: nobody wants to, but it's ridiculous for him to go
on wearing them because he doesn't need them any more.

Nobody wants to take them off.

They're wet and very cold and have a strange whiteness
to them that is absolutely silent.

He lies on the riverbank with his tennis shoes a few
inches from the water, the last thing that he ever knew,
filling him up with death.

Tokyo
July 14, 1978

The Great Golden Telescope

She has let herself go and she is thirty-five pounds over-weight. Her long dark hair is a tangled rebel against combs and brushes. Her wardrobe could be described as sloppy and desolate.

And all she wants to do is talk.

There are a bunch of us in a cabin: twelve or fourteen. The occasion is a very loose dinner party in the foothills of New Mexico, just outside of a small town.

The food is delicious.

We sit around on the floor eating it.

We all look like hippies.

On my way to the house, riding on the back of a truck, some spring snow fell. It was a slight flurry that didn't stick, and a short while later I watched a beautiful sunset from outside the house and I played with two kittens and a tom-cat and marvelled at how big New Mexico is.

Everything is very casual inside the house, low-geared,

mellow, except for the girl. She interrupts whatever we are talking about, which isn't very important stuff, but still after a while it gets on our nerves a little.

We are all very patient with her. She talks very slowly in a shy bumbling way. She is like having a difficult child about the house.

These are the things that she talks about:

1. We should all make our clothes out of a special seaweed that grows along the California coast. She has a notebook full of designs for seaweed clothes out in the Volkswagen bus. She will go and get the book after she has finished eating. Her three children are asleep in the bus. She never eats meat, so she is making an exception with this meal. They're very tired.

(It turns out later that nobody in the house had ever seen her before. She just came by and joined in. Maybe she smelled dinner when it was cooking and figured that this was a good place to park her bus for a while and get something to eat.)

2. We'll take the massive profits that will be earned from the seaweed clothes, everybody will want them, Dennis Hopper, he lives at Taos, and just everybody, maybe Frank Zappa too, and Carole King, and buy a mountain where people can live in peace and harmony with a great golden telescope. She knows right where the mountain is. It's a cheap mountain, too. It could be purchased for just a few hundred thousand dollars from the seaweed clothes profits.

(Nobody is really very interested in what she is talking about because it is such a familiar conversation that every-

[124]

body has heard again and again coming from people who have been wiped out by taking too many drugs or living a life style that's just too estranged from reality but somebody has to ask her about the telescope and they do, but . . .)

3. By this time she has gone onto something else and the future of the great golden telescope is in serious doubt.

(I take another bite of food.)

4. "Do you know what?" she says suddenly, having just told us a long story about the possibility of building boats that look like old-timey train engines like the ones you see in Western movies and shipping them by real four-wheeled trains to the California coast, where they would look beautiful anchored beside our seaweed boutiques, "I think I've been in a Volkswagen bus too long."

The Man Who Shot Jesse James

When I was a child I knew who killed Jesse James, shot him in the back when he was putting a picture up on the wall.

That man's name was as familiar to me as my own

because Jesse James was a hero of my youth. My friends and I used to talk about him being shot all the time. It was one of our favorite topics and always good for something to feel sad about or get angry at. Jesse James's death was as real and important to us as a death in the family.

But now at the age of forty-three I can't remember the name of the man who shot Jesse James. I've been trying to think of it all day but that name has remained out of sight in my mind, hiding somewhere in the canyons and crevasses of other memories.

I can remember that Pat Garrett shot Billy the Kid and the Dalton gang should never have gone to Coffeyville, Kansas, for a little banking where they were turned into bullet-riddled corpses stretched out on doors being photographed for posterity.

No one wants to have a photograph of themselves taken lying dead on a door in a Kansas street and be remembered that way.

. . . ugh.

You don't need it.

But that still leaves me not able to remember the name of the man who shot my boyhood hero Jesse James. I try desperately to think of his name.

Did it start with Matthew or Will or Sam or Richard . . . or I just don't know.

What I once knew and was so important to me, I can't remember now. It has been claimed and taken away by the forces of time, a Western myth gone like the buffalo with nothing to assume its place.

[126]

Dancing Feet

He is a businessman who comes to Tokyo three times a year. He is very interested in shoes. No, that's not his line of business. He is in some very strange way involved with computers, but still shoes are what he's really interested in. Actually, it's not shoes but feet: the feet of Japanese women. He is madly in love with their feet.

He comes to Japan three times a year to look at the feet that are in the shoes. When he is in Japan, which averages two weeks a visit, he hangs around shoe stores a lot, watching Japanese women trying on shoes. He also carefully studies the sidewalks of Tokyo as if they were art galleries because they exhibit shoes like moving sculpture and where there are shoes! Sometimes he wishes that he was a Japanese sidewalk. That would be paradise for him but could his heart stand the excitement of being a sidewalk?

In conventional storytelling this would be a good time to say some things about the life of the businessman: Maybe his age, country, background, family, does he masturbate? is he impotent? etc., but I won't because it's not important.

All that's important is that three times a year, he comes to Japan, spending two weeks looking at Japanese shoes and the feet inside of them. Of course, summertime is a must visit for him . . . sandals!

When the airplane flies him to Japan, he always gets a window seat and thousands of dancing feet pass by the window in shoes that bring out all their beauty.

Seventeen Dead Cats

When I was twelve years old in 1947, I had seventeen cats. There were tomcats, and mother cats, and kittens. I used to catch fish for them from a pond that was a mile away. The kittens liked to play with string under the blue sky.

Oregon 1947—California 1978

Light on at the Tastee-Freez

I saw a light on at the Tastee-Freez a few weeks ago and I've been thinking about it ever since. The Tastee-Freez has been closed since late October.

This is early March.

It will stay closed until the summer, June or sometime. I've only been here once when it reopened for the summer and that was a number of years ago and I was very busy at the time and I can't remember exactly when it opened.

Perhaps it opens as early as May or even earlier.

I don't know.

But one thing is for certain: until last year in October, they would always close just after Labor Day and it would be a signalling symbol to me that the summer was rapidly coming to a close here in Montana where spring, summer and autumn are so short and winter so very, very long.

They serve a good hamburger, the Big Tee burger and tasty onion rings and fifty flavors of milk shakes. You could have a different milk shake every day and almost two months would pass, like a Montana summer, before you would have to start over again with maybe Red Rose. That's one of the flavors they have or if you didn't want to start off with Red Rose, you could try a Grasshopper shake.

I'm not kidding.

Anyway, the Tastee-Freez used to close in early September and for some strange reason it would make me sad. I am growing older. There is one less summer in life with a closed sign on the door.

. . . no more Big Tees or the possibility of 700 different flavors of milk shakes . . .

After a while when they got to know what an enthusiastic fan of milk shakes you are, they might mix flavors together for you, opening up almost unlimited milk shake horizons stretching out to your first Red Rose-Grasshopper shake.

For these long winter months every time I drive by, the Tastee-Freez is closed and dark at night. That is, until a few weeks ago when I saw a light on as I drove by.

There was somebody inside the Tastee-Freez. Oh, I thought, maybe they're going to open up early this year and not wait until June or so, but open up in February. It was a good thought. It would almost be like an early summer coming to this snowy land of Montana.

The next day when I drove by, the closed sign was still on the door and that night the Tastee-Freez was dark inside again, and has remained that way ever since. It is definitely closed and probably will not open until May or

June or I don't know when but it is obvious they are not going to open up this winter.

Maybe the person who was in there that night was just checking the supplies, the milk shake flavors, for next summer or . . . who knows why somebody would turn the lights on at night in a Tastee-Freez that's been closed since late October?

But I continue thinking about it, not so much about what the person was doing in there but just that the light was on months before the Tastee-Freez would open.

Sometimes when people are talking to me about very important things like President Carter or the Panama Canal and think that I'm listening to them, I'm really thinking about the light on at the Tastee-Freez.

The Eyes of Japan

I am visiting a Japanese home outside of Tokyo. The people are very nice. The wife greets us at the door. Once she had been a very popular television star. She is still young and beautiful and retired now to married life and children.

[131]

We are a party of four people, including her husband. I am the only person who is not Japanese.

We are graciously, perfectly welcomed into the house and soon sitting in a Western-style dining room that is also part kitchen. His wife busies herself preparing food: little snacks, and getting us sake to drink. We have not been there any longer than just sitting down when her husband, a very kind and sweet man, says jokingly, "I am the lion of my own house."

I don't know what that means but I know it means something or it would not have been said. I have a feeling that it is for my benefit. I look around the house. It is modern and comfortable. The man is a famous Japanese actor.

Soon we are drinking sake on the rocks which is a good drink on a hot, humid Japanese June night. The wife continues busying herself. Now she is cooking things for us to eat and he helps her by cooking some things, too. They are a very efficient kitchen team. This could be a play.

After a while, there are a lot of good things to eat on the table. We eat, drink and talk away. There is nothing more for her to do. She has not sat down since the company arrived.

Now she sits down but she does not sit down at the table. She sits down maybe five feet away and listens to the conversation. I watch her sitting there five feet away from the table and I think about what her husband said jokingly when we arrived, "I am the lion of my own house."

I didn't know what it meant but I knew that it meant

something. Now I know what it means, watching her sit five feet away from the table, not joining us, but enjoying herself just the same.

I look into her eyes. They are dark and beautiful. They are happy eyes. She is glad that we have come. She has done her best to make us comfortable and now she is enjoying our presence.

In her eyes, I see the past of Japan. I see thousands of years of Japanese women, not sitting at the table and happy. As I write this, I can also see American women reading these words and grinding their teeth while thinking: *Oh, the poor downtrodden slave of male tyranny! Instead of waiting on them like a servant, she should kick them all in the balls!*

I can see the expression on their faces.

I can see their eyes filled with hatred that is so far away from this room.

The Magic of Peaches

How many stops?
How many stops?
How many stops?
To the reindeer
  station?

Yesterday I bought four peaches though I didn't need
them. When I went into the grocery store I did not have
any interest in peaches. I wanted to buy something else
but I can't remember now what it was.

I was walking through the fruit section to get what has
been forgotten when I saw the peaches. Peaches were not
my destination but I stopped and looked at them, anyway.
They were beautiful peaches but still that wasn't reason
enough for me to buy them. I have seen a lot of good-
looking peaches in my time.

Without thinking I picked up one of the peaches to feel

how firm it was, and it felt just right, but hundreds of peaches over dozens of years have felt the same way.

What was going to cause me to buy peaches that I did not need?

Then I smelled a peach and it smelled just like my childhood. I stood there travelling back as if on a railroad train into the past where a peach could be an extraordinary event, almost like a reindeer station with a herd of deer waiting patiently for the train on a summer's day and all carrying bags of peaches to the end of the line.

Times Square in Montana

PART ONE:

I write in a small room at the top of an old barn made out of redwood a long time ago, when many people were alive who are dead now: Billy the Kid, Louis Pasteur, Queen Victoria, Mark Twain, Emperor Meiji of Japan, and Thomas Edison.

There are no redwood trees in these mountains of Montana, so the wood was brought over from the Pacific Coast and made into this huge barn which is over three stories high if stories is the right word to apply to the height of a barn.

The foundation of the barn is made out of glacial rocks placed in perfect companionship to each other to hold the redwood and all the things that are a barn up to the constantly changing Montana sky where I sit writing just a few feet below it.

The rocks also form a huge basement for the barn, which is kind of unusual because not many barns have a basement. The basement to this barn is another world best left to another time.

Later . . .

To get to my writing room high in this barn there is a flight of stairs that are almost metaphysical in their design climbing step-by-step starkly like death and desire up to just below the sky which now is filled with falling snow.

The stairs are divided into two landings and I have a railing, so I won't fall off the barn on my way to writing or when returning.

. . . not a good idea.

There is a light bulb at the top of the first landing where the stairs turn to go up another flight ending at a second light bulb.

I have a switch in the barn and a switch at the top of the stairs. It is a two-way switch, so that I can control the lights from the barn or at the top of the stairs, either way.

[136]

When I turn the switch on, the barn is bathed in a beautiful reddish light like a sundown from the wood and I am illuminated in my comings and goings.

I like to turn the switch on and off. It is very dramatic because the stairs are a cream-colored pine shining like a bridge against the redwood sunset and an important junction in my day-to-day life here in Montana.

[A slight meandering here because I just wanted to say that there are birds living in this barn that keep me company and there are some rabbits spending the winter downstairs where the hay for the horses is stored. There are little outcroppings of rabbit shit lying in mushroom-like designs in the loose hay from the bales. Sometimes when I feel lonely it is comforting to know that there are rabbits sharing my huge literary house, though I have never seen one, just their perfect poetic shit. Let's return to the lights.]

I receive pleasure from turning the lights on and off when coming and going from words like these. For some reason unknown to me I have been using bulbs of low wattage to shine my way.

Yesterday I discovered that the bulb at the top of the first landing was only 25 watts and the bulb at the top of the second landing where my room is, was only 75 watts, for a total of 100 watts of seeing power.

I thought about it after I finished writing and decided to increase the wattage and consequently the light in the barn. Last night after watching a high school basketball game in town, I went to a store that is open 24 hours a day and bought two light bulbs, which was one of the greatest adventures of my life.

I originally thought of increasing the bulbs to 150 watts, knowing all the time that 100 watts apiece would be a dramatic change, especially at the top of the first landing which had had a 25 watt globe for God only knows how long.

Maybe years . . .

Who keeps track of light bulb anniversaries these days, not unless you suddenly notice that you haven't changed a bulb in say, fifty years? Then you pay some attention, call out the media, but mostly you just forget about it. There are other things to think about: Does my wife love me? Why does she laugh a little too loud at my jokes when I know they aren't that funny or what am I going to do with the rest of my life?

Things other than light bulbs take up our time, which is not unreasonable.

Anyway, there I was standing in the light bulb section gazing fondly at wattage. From the way I looked you might think I was a collector of electric postage stamps and was just adding some very rare ones to my collection. Two 100 watt bulbs would be very adequate, but then I got to thinking why not go for some dramatic lighting like 150 watt bulbs?

That would really be something to see when I turned them on at night for the first time. The barn would explode in light like a Broadway play.

I liked that idea a lot, and then I saw some 200 watt bulbs. My heart almost skipped a beat like a critic falling in love with a play.

200 watt bulbs!

What an opportunity for fun!

I could light up my Montana redwood barn just like Times Square. Why settle for a Broadway play when you can have one of the world's most famous theater districts in your barn?

I bought the two bulbs with an eager anticipation for the next day when I would put them in the barn and the next night when I would turn them on for the first time.

Well, now it's the day of that night, eleven o'clock, and the hours pass here in Montana for night to come and then Times Square in my barn.

These are the pleasures of my life.

I wait like a child for my electric light dessert.

PART TWO:

I waited through the day, and night came to Montana as it always does . . . and the moment to Times-Square my barn with a Great White Way of 200 watt bulbs, all two of them.

I had told my wife about the bulbs and my excitement to see the barn shining like Broadway and she got a daffodil from a bunch we'd bought in town earlier and put it in a little old bottle and we headed out through the snow to the barn. I had a feeling of magic in my hand as I

[139]

touched the switch and the barn exploded into light, bathed in bounty like Times Square.

"It's beautiful," she said.

I was so proud of the light that I couldn't think of anything to say. We started upstairs. She was walking in front of me, carrying the daffodil.

We reached the top of the first landing and I looked at the light bulb shining away. I felt like stroking it as if it were a cat, and if I did, I knew that it would start purring.

We walked up the second flight of stairs and just as we reached the top, the light blew out. My heart dropped like a stone into a cold well.

"Oh, no!" I said, staring in disbelief at the suddenly, eternally gone light bulb.

My wife had a sympathetic expression on her face. She was showing empathy because she knew how much that light bulb meant to me.

I opened the door to my writing room and I turned the light on in there and she put the daffodil on the desk.

I was still in a state of shock.

She said something which I can't remember to try and make me feel better about the bulb burning out. It was as if half of Times Square had gone out at midnight, a blackout, leaving people in a state of surprise and shock.

Just after she finished saying that which was very nice— too bad I have forgotten what it was—there was another flash in the barn like a small explosion.

Through a window in my writing room that looks back into the barn where the flash had come from, I could see that the stairs were dark.

"Oh, no!"

I opened the door and all of Times Square was gone. The other 200 watt bulb had blown out, too.

"Poor man," my wife said.

I found the 25 watt bulb that I had retired in my room and screwed it in at the top of the stairs, just outside the door.

We made our way down the stairs.

There was a dim bulb on the main floor of the barn that helped provide us with enough light so as not to make it a hazardous journey.

As we went down, I retrieved the two burnt-out bulbs. "You know what I'm going to do with these bulbs?" I said to my wife, my voice reflecting anger.

"No," she said, cautiously. She's Japanese and sometimes she gets cautious when I make dramatic announcements. She comes from a different culture. The Japanese do not respond to life the way I do. "What are you going to do?" she said.

"Take them back to the store and get some more bulbs."

"Do you think they'll accept them?"

"Yes," I said, my voice rising. "They don't work! LIGHT BULBS SHOULD LAST LONGER THAN TEN SECONDS!"

I don't think she really thought that I was going to do it. The idea of a store accepting and exchanging burnt-out light bulbs seemed like a foreign idea to her. I don't think that was a common practice in Japan, but right now I didn't care about Japan. I had been wronged and I wanted satisfaction.

[141]

We were going to town to watch another basketball game that evening, so I put the bulbs in a paper bag, along with the receipt for the bulbs and took them into town with me.

After the game, we stopped at the store.

She still didn't believe that I was going to try and exchange two burnt-out light bulbs. She thought of a convenient reason to stay out in the car and I stormed into the store carrying a paper bag with two burnt-out light bulbs in it.

The store was huge and abandoned because it was after ten and there was a snowstorm going on in Montana. People were not interested in shopping at that time and under those conditions, and I think this was ultimately to my advantage.

There was a middle-aged lady at the checkout counter. She was just standing there with a dreamy-late-February-night expression on her face, no customers and not much prospect of getting any.

Then I was standing there with my paper bag in my hands. I was carrying the bag in such a way as to return her from wherever she was dreaming to the direct reality of the store and somebody mysteriously appearing out of a winter storm holding a paper bag dramatically in his hands.

"Can I help you?" she said automatically, and probably hoping that I wasn't some kind of crazed stick-up man with a bomb in a bag on a winter night.

"These light bulbs," I said, reaching into the bag and taking out two light bulbs. "They burned out within a few seconds after I turned them on," I said. I put the bulbs down on the counter. She stared at them. I don't think anyone had ever walked out of a snowstorm and put two burnt-out light bulbs on her counter before.

It was a first.

"I put them in the barn," I said. "It's wired for 220 and I have circuit breakers but the bulbs just burnt out. They lasted for only a few seconds. I think light bulbs should last longer than that. I'd like to return them," I said, already having returned them because they were now lying on the counter between the checker and me. Now I would have to see what would happen.

My wife waited in the car, probably re-examining her decision to marry me or at least looking at it in a different perspective.

"Sounds reasonable to me," the woman said.

One of life's victories had just fallen into my hands!

"Do you want to see the receipt?" I said, thinking that it would add a nice professional touch to it all.

"No," she said. "That's not necessary. I remember you."

That was interesting because I didn't remember her. I wonder why she remembered me. Oh, well, it was just another life detail better left banished to oblivion.

"Do you want your money back or two more light bulbs?" she said.

"I want two more light bulbs," I said. "But I don't want 200 watters. I don't trust them. I want 150 watt bulbs. I have faith in them."

I had learned my lesson about experimental light bulbs.

[143]

I had never seen a 200 watt bulb before and I didn't want to see another one again. I would stick to the traditional ways of light.

Times Square was a good idea but if it didn't work, what good was it? I would retreat to the electric power of a Broadway play in my barn.

That would satisfy me.

A total wattage increase from 100 watts to 300 watts would be enough for me and my barn.

After I got the two 150 watt bulbs, we had to make a price adjustment because the 200 watt bulbs were more expensive. The transaction was an exchange of a few pennies.

I went out and got into the car with an air of triumph carrying a different bag with my two new light bulbs.

"What happened?" my Japanese wife said.

I held the bag toward her.

"Electric *sushi*," I said.

. . .

Today I put the two 150 watt bulbs in the barn and now I will wait again for night to come and to see my barn light up like a Broadway play.

. . . hopefully.

PART THREE:

My barn just opened like a Broadway play, the hottest ticket in town, when I turned the lights on. These two 150 watt bulbs are like starring John Barrymore and Sarah

Bernhardt in a tap-dancing version of *Hamlet* with original
music composed and played by Mozart.

What a ticket!

My barn tonight.

Wind in the Ground

I have admired the Japanese novelist for years and at my
request somebody has arranged this meeting between us.
We are having dinner in a Tokyo restaurant. Suddenly,
the novelist reaches into a bag he is carrying and takes out
a pair of goggles and puts them on.

Now: The two of us are sitting across from each other
and he is wearing a pair of goggles. The people in the restaurant are staring at us. I act as if it is perfectly natural for
a man to be wearing a pair of goggles in a restaurant, but I
am thinking very gently, and directing a single thought at
him: *Please take the fucking goggles off.*

I don't say a word about him wearing the goggles. My
face does not betray what I am thinking. I admire him so

The Last of My
Armstrong Spring Creek
Mosquito Bites

The last of my Armstrong Spring Creek mosquito bites fade quickly from my body like the end of a movie leaving the screen.

I'm here on the California coast. It's foggy. The Pacific crashes. I'm far away from that beautiful creek outside of Livingston, Montana, where the sunset echoed off the mountains to remain in my eyes longer than its existence.

I could still see the sunset after it was gone.

The mosquitoes bit the hell out of me a few evenings ago while I explored a hatch of May flies like an astronomer but instead of discovering a new comet, I hooked a good German brown trout on my rod.

I lost him but I didn't feel bad because I've come to

[148]

know that there isn't enough space in your life to keep everything.

You'd run out of room.

Good-bye, mosquito bites.

Clouds over Egypt

A train is travelling from Cairo to Alexandria. It is a blue sky, white cloud day in Egypt. I am watching the train on television here in California, a long way from the Middle East.

Why do Egyptian clouds catch my attention as I look at the train? These are the first clouds I remember seeing in weeks or maybe months. I just haven't been paying attention. When did I stop?

The train is carrying the President of the United States Jimmy Carter and the President of Egypt Anwar Sadat. They are trying to find peace between Egypt and Israel. It's somewhere out there in the desert. While they are doing this, I am watching clouds and trying to figure out what they mean to my life.

[149]

We all have our roles in history.
Mine is clouds.

Fantasy Ownership

This is a little study in power. It is something I have observed before in America, but especially here in Tokyo.

The subject is waitresses.

I'll go into a Japanese restaurant that serves nothing but eels cooked in a dozen different ways and all the waitresses will be short, squat and slightly plump with round moon-like Japanese faces.

I'll go into another restaurant and all the waitresses will be tall, slender and with long Japanese faces. It will be a restaurant specializing in noodles.

A third restaurant will have Chinese food served by waitresses with large breasts and very small eyes and full mouths. They could almost be sisters but they aren't.

It must be interesting to own a restaurant in Tokyo, like owning a fantasy.

[150]

The Mill Creek Penguins

I have been fishing in the same neighborhood of Mill Creek for six years now. One particular stream corner has always been very good to me. If I had a newspaper stand there among the rocky blue and green of the creek flow, business would have been quite successful for a fisherman reader with headlines like:

WHY READ *THE NEW YORK TIMES?*
SIX GOOD TROUT CAUGHT RIGHT HERE

Last night was the middle of October and a warm autumn sun was going down and I was fishing my favorite spot. Most of the leaves had fallen from the brush close to the creek. I fished for twenty minutes or so and had two rises and caught them both.

One trout was a very fat sixteen inches which I consider an excellent fish for Mill Creek and he put up a good

[151]

fight. When I first reached my spot, I caught a ten-inch fish immediately. Then there was a fifteen minute wait, like waiting for an Izaak Walton bus, before I caught the big one. During that period I kept up a steady typing on the stream with my fly rod while my mind drifted from place to place, past and present watching the fly as if it were my imagination and the creek and its bank products of that imagination.

Suddenly something moved in the fallen leafy confusion of the underbrush across the creek, and I thought it was a penguin. I didn't actually see what moved. I only saw the movement, but for some reason or another I thought that it was a penguin.

Montana is known for moose, grizzly bears, elk, antelope, etc. You can practically name it but no penguins. Penguins are the butlers of the Antarctic as if a trillionaire lived there and employed them all. They have no business in Montana, not unless they are in zoos at Billings or Great Falls.

Why a penguin? And as I said earlier: I actually did not even see it. I saw only a movement that I thought was a penguin. Needless to say I was quite relieved when I caught the sixteen-inch trout that put up a good fight before I let it go.

That trout made sense.

I wonder if when I fish that place on Mill Creek again, I will be indirectly, subconsciously keeping my eye open for a penguin. I will find out next year because I don't plan on going back there this year.

[152]

A Reason for Living

I knew that the son-of-a-bitch had to be good for something, that there must be a reason for him to exist, and I finally found one today.

I think he works for a company here in Tokyo and I think he is from Australia. Whenever I go to a certain café to write in Harajuku, I'll see him if I am still there after 5 p.m.

He is in his early thirties and very good looking, actually handsome, in a sort of obvious, predictable way that is skin deep. He possesses a style that is modeled after images of certain men he has seen in the movies and on television. I don't think that the bastard can read.

He is probably a very important man for some business in Tokyo. Maybe he is the vice-president and has many people at his beckoning, but you don't think I believe that, do you?

Anyway, he arrives after 5 and emits like a gas a sort of

false charm that he very carefully holds in arrogant restraint as if he were doing the planet a favor.

Being cool: I believe is the word and I overhear him talking to other foreigners that inhabit the place, and of course he often meets women there or they arrive with him.

He makes it a special point for them to know what a cool guy he is by almost totally ignoring them. He arrives with or meets a girl there and then he spends his time talking to other foreigners.

There is always a mirror at the table where he sits and he never lets his own image get out of his sight: Everything he does like lighting a cigarette or taking a sip of beer or pausing a long time before saying something stupid, he watches in the mirror.

Once he was with a very pretty Japanese woman and when they left the place he walked off as if she wasn't with him. She had stopped to look at something and he just continued walking away. When she looked up, he was almost gone. "Where are you going!" she yelled.

Good girl. When she said that I liked her immediately, and as you can see, this guy has gotten on my nerves, though we have never said a word or even recognized each other's existence.

Today I was sitting there at the café when he arrived early. It was 4 o'clock. I almost wondered what was up, why his routine had been disturbed, almost, and then he sat down right beside me and of course there was no recognition.

[154]

He sat there.

I sat there.

I think he dislikes me, too, because I obviously don't belong at the café. I look like a fading middle-aged hippie and never talk to anybody except the young Japanese men who work there.

I know the prick is also a snob.

Anyway, today I finally found out why he was put on this earth. I had to meet somebody later at 6 o'clock in another part of Tokyo and I don't even own a watch and from where he was sitting I could see his watch, so from time to time, keeping track of my future appointment, I looked at his watch.

As I said earlier: I knew that the son-of-a-bitch must be of some earthly good, a reason for him to live.

1953 Chevrolet

No seats, no fenders, no rearview mirror, no headlights, no brakes, no bumpers, no tires, no trunk, no windshield wipers, no windshield

Inspired by a vision of poetic American romance, my friend was interested in buying an old car in Montana and driving it back to California. Every evening he would get a copy of the local newspaper and look in the want ads for an old car that could get to California.

CALIFORNIA OR BUST!

He was thinking in a price range of maybe two or three hundred dollars with a four-hundred-dollar tops.

That's not much for a car in this year of 1978 but my friend had a dream of an old car going happily down the road to California with still a few months of driving left in it after getting there.

A good old Montana car like a good old boy.

One evening he saw an ad that really wetted his romance:

1953 CHEVROLET $50

He immediately called up the telephone number in the ad and got the voice of an old woman. "You have a 1953 Chevrolet for sale?" he said. "For fifty dollars?"

"That's right," she said. "It's in perfect condition."

"I'd like to look at it," he said.

"Yes," she said. "You can't buy it not unless you see it. I live on North L Street," and she gave him the address.

"When can I look at it?" he said.

"You can come now," she said.

"OK, I'll be there in twenty minutes," he said.

"All right," she said. "I'll be expecting you. What's your name again?"

[156]

"Reynolds," he said.

"All right, Mr. Reynolds. I'll see you soon."

My friend hung up, very excited: $50!

In his mind he saw himself driving to California in the most beautiful 1953 Chevrolet left in America:

A real sweetheart with only 15,000 miles on the speedometer because the old woman only drove the car to the store three times a week and to church on Sunday.

A car with its original whitewall tires in perfect running condition.

He was madly in love with that car by the time he arrived at the address on North L Street. He felt like a teenager going out on his first date with the prettiest cheerleader in high school.

The old woman answered the door.

She was very old but could still get around, sprightly is the word.

"Hello," he said. "I'm the man who called you about the 1953 Chevrolet. Mr. Reynolds is my name."

"Hello, Mr. Reynolds," she said. "I'll show it to you."

She put a coat on and stepped outside and led him around the house to the garage.

"How are the tires?" he said, trying to hide his excitement but failing.

"There are no tires," she answered.

"No tires," my friend said. "Oh."

That knocked a little hole in his dream. He would have to buy some tires for the car but he knew that it would be such a wonderful bargain old car that buying some tires for it would be a small matter, hardly big enough to be con-

[157]

sidered. After all, it would be a car in perfect running condition. Tires were no big deal. He mentally subtracted the tires from the picture of the car in his mind.

"What about the brakes?" he said.

"There are no brakes."

"What? No brakes?" he said.

"That's right," she said. "No brakes."

"No brakes?" he repeated.

"No brakes."

He mentally subtracted brakes from his dream car that already had no tires and moved on to another thing in his mind but then he doubled back and thought about it again: No tires? No brakes?

Then without thinking he said to the old lady, "What shape is the body in?"

"No body," she said.

"No tires, no brakes, no body," he chanted like a child.

"That's right," she said, acting as if it were a perfectly normal car to sell somebody.

He had met some pretty crafty used-car dealers in his time but this old lady took the cake. What in the hell kind of car was she trying to sell him?

"Why doesn't it have a body?" he said, automatically like a child.

"Because it's not a car," she said.

"What?" he said as she led him through the garage door into where an automobile engine greeted them. The engine was lying on the floor in the middle of the garage.

"That's a 1953 Chevrolet?" he said.

[158]

"Engine," she said.

"Engine?" he said.

"Yes, engine," she said.

"I thought you were advertising a car for sale," he said.

"Why would I do that?" she said. "I don't have a car. I just have an engine. Fifty dollars. Do you want to buy it?"

"I'm interested in buying a car," he said. "I want to drive it to California."

"Well," she said, motioning toward the engine. "You can't drive this to California, not unless you get the rest of it."

Thank you, ma'am.

My friend went home and got the newspaper and turned to the want ad section and looked up the ad for the 1953 Chevrolet. He read it half a dozen times. He examined every word in the ad very carefully as if he were reading a first edition of the Bible in Chinese and wanted to make sure that it was an accurate translation.

Then he called the old woman back up on the telephone. Her telephone kept ringing but she didn't answer it. He let the telephone ring for a long time before he hung up.

She's probably showing it to somebody else? he thought. He could see them walking around to the garage. He could hear somebody saying to her, "How's the engine?"

And her replying, "It's in perfect condition."

[159]

My Fair Tokyo Lady

TEA TIME . . .

I saw a stage production of *My Fair Lady* in Tokyo in Japanese and performed by an all-Japanese cast. I fell in love with the Japanese actors and actresses singing and dancing in front of sets and backdrops of Victorian London.

At one point, a handsome Rex Harrison-type Japanese Professor Higgins was standing on the front porch of a London house in the 1890s beside a backdrop street of other London houses and he was singing a song in Japanese about, I think, his love for a Japanese Eliza Doolittle.

I wondered if the backdrop houses were filled with Victorian Japanese listening to him sing and hoping that it would all work out for the best.

I looked into the windows of the backdrop houses but saw no one staring out and nobody came out onto any of the front porches and the street was empty. Maybe everyone was in the back gardens of the houses, having tea.

[160]

Other people have their lives, too. They just can't stand around listening to people sing, especially if it isn't any of their business.

NIGHTBORN . . .

My imagination is having a love affair with people moving swiftly and efficiently in the dark. Their every movement is calculated, like a saint to achieve the maximum amount of effect.

In other words: They know what they are doing like the nightborn tides of the sea. The character of their actions resembles the work of spies getting things done in the dark.

When their work is done and the stage lights come back on and the play continues, the actors are no longer in the drawing room of an elegant Victorian mansion but they are in a poor section of London.

I think if I had not become a writer, I would like to have been a stagehand moving around like a spy magician in the dark, taking furniture away: a couch, a desk, a piano in the dark, and replacing it with the streets of London when the lights return.

THE ACTOR ONE MILLION YEARS FROM NOW . . .

I am very carefully watching the actor who is playing a part older than his actual age. His hair has been frosted with some kind of white stuff and then he is suitable, proper for the age of the part.

[161]

In actuality what makes you older is when your bones, muscles and blood wear out, when the heart sinks into oblivion and all the houses you ever lived in are gone and people are not really certain that your civilization ever existed.

The Menu / 1965

California has a population explosion on its hands. There are close to 20,000,000 people in California and forty-eight men on Death Row at San Quentin. In 1952 there were twenty-two men on Death Row and the population of California was 11,000,000 people. If things continue at this rate, in the year 2411 there will be 500,000,000 people in California and 2,000 men on Death Row.

I was over at San Quentin a couple of days ago talking to Mr. Lawrence Wilson who is the warden of the prison. He was a little annoyed when he said, looking up and in the direction of Death Row, "There are forty-eight men on Death Row and the courts keep sending us more. If we execute the men we have there now, that will be more people than were executed last year in the entire country."

Warden Wilson has a problem. California has not executed a man since January 23, 1963, when a farm laborer named James Bentley exhausted all the possibilities of being a California citizen.

Of the forty-eight men now on Death Row, over half of them have been there for two years or more. A couple of men, Manuel Chavez and Clyde Bates, have been there since 1957. Years pass in California before the condemned get to the gas chamber. Caryl Chessman was on Death Row for so long that they were thinking about giving him a pension.

Death Row, California. What does it mean to me as a writer and as a citizen of this state? I decided to find out. I called up San Quentin and talked to Associate Warden James Park. I asked him if I could visit Death Row.

In a friendly, almost folksy voice, he said to me that it was frowned on. "They have a closed community," he said. "They get upset when strangers come around looking at the critters in the zoo." But Mr. Park did offer to show me the gas chamber. I guess that's some consolation.

I went over to San Quentin a few days later. I wanted to see how far I could go toward achieving a perfect vision of Death Row.

James Park is a clinical psychologist who graduated from UCLA, and he offered me a cup of tea in his office. He is a relaxed and articulate man. He was wearing a very nice striped tie.

[163]

"What do the men eat on Death Row?" I asked. I was not interested in last meals, but in the food they were eating today. I figured the most important thing in a prison was the food.

"Well, let's see," Mr. Park said. He got up and went into the main office. He went to a filing cabinet and came back with the week's menu.

Seeing DEPARTMENT OF CORRECTIONS on top of the menu and then "Weekly Menu for CONDEMNED ROW" underneath gave me a strange feeling. It was almost a functioning intimacy with death in one of its more complicated forms, and there was a dramatic quality to the April 16th dinner.

Beef Noodle Soup
Cole Slaw
Sour Cream Dressing
Grilled Halibut Steak
Cocktail Sauce
Chicken Fried Steak
Rissotto
Btrd. Cauliflower

"May I have this menu?" I asked.
"I guess so," Mr. Park said.
I asked him what the caloric content of the food was on Death Row. He called somebody on the telephone. "What's the caloric content of the food on Death Row? The mainline is 4200, huh. You'd guess about 4500 calories. OK. Thank you."

[164]

State of California

DEPARTMENT OF CORRECTIONS

CALIFORNIA STATE PRISON AT SAN QUENTIN

Name of Facility

Weekly Menu For ...CONDEMNED ROW...

Name of Dining Room   Date 4-1-65 From 4-12-65 To 4-16-65

Prepared By *H. H. Mc Daniel*   APPROVED: *R. Small*

H.H. MCDANIEL, SUPERVISING COOK II   R. SMALL, FOOD MANAGER

	BREAKFAST	DINNER	SUPPER
12 Monday	Stewed Prunes Farina Boiled Eggs Crisp Bacon Hot Cakes Maple Syrup Toast - Bread - Oleo Coffee - Milk	Split Pea Soup Waldorf Salad Cream Dressing Barbecue Shortribs Grilled Wieners Mustard Sauce Spaghetti Italian Btrd. Spinach	Lima Beans Ice Cream - Cookies Frankfurter Buns Bread Oleo Coffee Milk Peanut Butter Sandwich
13 Tuesday	Tomato Juice Branflakes Scrambled Eggs Crisp Bacon Creamed Beef Toast Bread - Oleo Coffee - Milk	Spaghetti Soup Beet & Onion Salad Vinaigrette Dressing Roast Leg O Pork Brown Sauce Ground Round Steak Mashed Potatoes Cream Style Corn	Pork & Beans Almond Tarts Bread Oleo Coffee Milk Apples Salami Sandwich
14 Wednesday	Stewed Figs Cracked Wheat Fried Eggs Breakfast Steak Breakfast Roll Jelly Toast - Bread - Oleo Coffee - Milk	Cream of Tomato Soup Potato Salad Mayonnaise Dressing Cold Cuts Swiss Liver Onion Gravy Rissole Potato Braised Cabbage	Red Beans Orange Cake Garlic Roll Bread Oleo Coffee Milk Cheese Sandwich
15 Thursday	Pear Halves Farina Cheese Omelet Crisp Bacon Lyonnaise Potatoes Toast Bread - Oleo Coffee - Milk	Scotch Broth Pineapple Cott.Ch.Salad Cream Dressing Hungarian Goulash W/Noodles Lamb Cutlets Tamale Loaf Btrd. Broccoli	Lima Beans Boston Cream Pie Bread Oleo Coffee Milk Oranges Olive Loaf Sandwich
16 Friday	Stewed Peaches Rolled Oats Fried Eggs Crisp Bacon Hot Cross Buns Jam Toast - Bread - Oleo Coffee - Milk	Beef Noodle Soup Cole Slaw Sour Cream Dressing Grilled Halibut Steak Cocktail Sauce Chicken Fried Steak Risotto Btrd. Cauliflower	Navy Beans Apple Raisin Pie Dinner Rolls Bread Oleo Coffee Milk Pork Loaf Sandwich
17 Saturday	California Orange Cornflakes Plain Omelet Crisp Bacon French Toast Maple Syrup Toast - Bread - Oleo Coffee - Milk	Beef Broth W/Rice Combination Salad Wine Vinegar Dressing Pot Roast of Beef Brown Sauce Grilled Pork Chops Creamed Potatoes Succotash	Mexican Beans Ice Cream Cookies Bread Oleo Coffee Milk Pimiento Loaf Sandwich
18 Sunday	Stewed Mixed Fruit Rolled Wheat Colored Easter Eggs Crisp Bacon Hash Brown Potatoes Country Gravy Toast - Bread - Oleo Coffee - Milk	Lentil Soup Italian Green Salad Garlic Dressing Raisin Sauce Baked Ham Snowflake Potatoes Btrd. Green Peas Chili Bowl	Chocolate Cake Bread Oleo Coffee Milk Apples Cheese Sandwich

Population: Remarks:

Guests ....   Menu Rating Very Interesting ....   Interesting ....

Employees ....   Satisfactory ....   Fairly Satisfactory ....

Inmates ....   Poor ....

4500 calories. How strange, I thought. That's a lot of calories for somebody who's going to live a sedentary existence, and it's not true about the world loving a fat man. Or was Death Row different?

Then I asked him about television on Death Row. He told me that they have a television set for every three cells and the men have remote control devices in their cells so they can change the channels if they want to. There are earphones for the sound and they can watch movies all night on Channel 7.

He told me that the men were influenced by the advertising on television and will suddenly start ordering a certain product from the canteen after it's been advertised on television.

I had an immediate vision of the prisoners of Death Row all ordering brand-new Fords from the canteen.

"What's the favorite food on Death Row?" I asked.

Mr. Park called a guard on the telephone.

"Uh-huh. Mexican food. And steaks. They get steaks twice a week."

After a while Warden Wilson came in and we all sat around and talked about Death Row, capital punishment, the courts, the gas chamber, rich people and poor people and the difference between them when they start murdering other people and what happens then. It's all been repeated a billion times and we repeated it once more.

But I found the tamale loaf that was going to be served Thursday for dinner on Death Row far more exciting than the fact that ninety percent of the prison administrators in the country are against capital punishment.

I was by now holding the menu in my lap, and even then, as we talked about Death Row, I knew the menu was my equipment for a perfect vision of Death Row. I knew that I could go a long way on the menu, and that's what I planned on doing.

Associate Warden Park showed me a "good" book to read called *The Death Penalty in America*, but it did not look nearly as interesting as the roast leg of pork on Tuesday.

Finally, I took *my* menu and left. I was no longer curious as to how many Death Rows could stand on the end of a needle. I wanted to know something else. Returning to San Francisco on the bus, I cradled the menu gently in my lap and carefully planned its future.

That evening a friend came over to my house. He's an aspiring Hollywood scriptwriter and he was looking for someone to type a manuscript of his, so he could sell it to the movies and become rich and famous and invite me to come stay with him in LA, and think the good thoughts while floating around in his new swimming pool.

Before he found a typist, we were sitting in the kitchen drinking dark April-like bock beer. It was not by accident that I showed him the Death Row menu. It was time for the menu to go to work. I just handed it to him and said, "Take a look at this."

"What do you have there, Richard?" He took a look at the menu and it did not please him. His face tensed and became a nervous gray. "That's the Pop Art that hurts," he said.

"You think so, huh?" I said.

[167]

"Yes, it's sick," he said. "It's like that sculpture. You know the kind that has drawers full of dead babies."

The menu was lying in front of him on the table and it said that for breakfast on Saturday the men on Death Row would have a

California Orange
Cornflakes
Plain Omelet
Crisp Bacon
French Toast
Maple Syrup
Toast—Bread—Oleo
Coffee—Milk

My friend's reaction to the menu assured me that I was on the right track. This menu was a very powerful and strange experience. I must find other things that it can do, I thought.

The next day I showed the menu to some poet friends of mine. They are gentle poets who live in an old Victorian house surrounded by trees and sometimes they do not have enough food to eat. We were all sitting in the kitchen.

One of the poets looked at the menu very carefully for a long time and then said, "It's frightening, obscene and disgusting."

The other poet looked at the menu and said, "Look at all that food. I love crisp bacon. I haven't had any bacon in a year. Look at all that food. The men up there must really get fat. It's like nailing the goose to the floor and then feeding him to death. Why don't they give this food to a poet?"

"Because a poet didn't kill anyone," the other poet replied.

Ah, to journey with a Death Row menu through the streets of San Francisco and to nurture its expanding vision, its search for new reality in a tired old thing.

I carried the menu in a Manila envelope past innocent and unassuming people going to the store to buy halibut steak for dinner and then to fall asleep while watching television on Channel 7.

I visited another friend. He works at night and we had a cup of coffee together. We gossiped and got caught up with our lives and then I said, "I want to show you something."

"Sure."

I took out the menu and handed it to him. He read the menu and his face changed from a sitting-here-having-a-cup-of-coffee face to a very serious face.

"What do you think?" I said.

"It's so stark, so real," he said. "It's like a poem. This menu alone condemns our society. To feed somebody this kind of food who is already effectively dead represents all the incongruity of the whole damn thing. It's senseless."

I looked down at the menu lying there on the table and for dinner Tuesday the men on Death Row were having

Spaghetti Soup
Beet and Onion Salad
Vinaigrette Dressing

[169]

Roast Leg O Pork
Brown Sauce
Ground Round Steak
Mashed Potatoes
Cream Style Corn
etc.

And this to become senseless? How could beet and onion salad condemn our society? I always thought we were a little stronger than that. Was it possible for this menu to be a menace to California if it fell into the wrong hands?

I spent the day showing the menu to people, curious and travelling all over San Francisco and leaving in my wake the food for seven days on Death Row.

Finally, I ended up at the house of a friend who is a straight-A student at San Francisco State College. His daughter was playing on the floor. She was wearing a very beautiful striped shirt.

She was reciting her letters from an alphabet book while her father read the menu. He read it slowly and with precision. Actually he was hunched over it.

"S is for Santa Claus."

She is a bright little girl four years old and looks like Clara Bow come to visit us again in child form.

"It's a menu," her father said, after he had finished reading the menu. "And a menu is the description of a meal that never existed."

My friend is an intellectual who takes a fierce but quiet

pride in the use of intelligence. He's pleased by his brain.

"It's not a salad," he said, pointing at a salad on the menu. "It's the obligation of a salad to be fulfilled."

"I guess you can look at it that way," I said.

His wife came home from work. She works at a hospital and she looked tired. The day had been very long. I showed the menu to her. As she looked at it, her mouth twitched and her face grimaced. "Horrible," she said. "It's horrible. Just horrible," and handed it back to me as if it were something vile, pornographic.

After a while the little girl put her alphabet book down. She was tired of it. As a kind of sad finale, she said hopelessly, "N is for Nest up in the tree."

Her father and I were talking about the menu. We had a long conversation about reality being twice removed from the menu. It was a long and deep conversation where the menu became a kind of thought diving bell going deeper and deeper, deeper and deeper until we were at the cold flat bottom of the sea, staring fish-like at the colored Easter eggs that were going to be served next Sunday on Death Row.

The Convention

Last week I saw two Japanese dwarfs on the same day, maybe an hour apart, walking along the same street. They were a perfect study of random chance, an example of how life is completely out of control.

You never know what is going to happen next.

I have always been fascinated by dwarfs. Whenever I see a dwarf, it almost takes my breath away. To me they are like watching magic. Many people think that dwarfs are like little children. That is one of their first thoughts, but not one of mine.

I can never imagine a dwarf ever having had a childhood. I think they were born just the way they are and are actually about sixty years old. I believe they were that old when they were born and learning how to talk was not a problem because they already knew how.

When I say these things, I am very carefully telling what I think. I don't want to hurt anyone. I know that they are feeling, compassionate human beings who have to deal with extraordinary problems. I would never dare take that away from them.

But still they are magic to me . . .

Maybe there was a convention of dwarfs in Tokyo and I saw the entire convention an hour apart from each other.

In Pursuit of
the Impossible Dream

I don't know why I think she should be at home with her child. They have as much right to walk around as I do, perhaps even more. A child needs to get out of the house, not stay indoors until it becomes the faded wafer of a child.

But still . . .

I see her on the street more times than often, always with her child. She is about thirtyish and I think some kind of European. She has fading good looks, her edges

[173]

are turning in, and a tooth is missing. I don't know why she doesn't replace the tooth. It's not that she's poor. This is a good neighborhood and she doesn't look out of place.

I have a couple of teeth missing, too, and I certainly can't blame her for it. Why don't I replace my teeth? So as you can see, there is more here than meets the eye.

Her child is a very animated little girl who is always cheerfully dressed and clean as a whistle. There's no reason for me to get upset when I see them, and who am I to judge how often and how long they can wander around outside?

But still . . .

I see them half a dozen or a dozen times a day and I can guarantee you that I do not go out looking for them. I don't set the alarm clock. I don't carry around a timetable and I certainly do not use a stopwatch!

But still . . .

I wonder how many times I don't see them. Of course I know that life is not easy, it is not what we planned, and I must not forget that whenever I am seeing them, they are also seeing me.

The Old Testament Book
of the Telephone Company

We all have adventures with the telephone company that could be right out of the Old Testament: things along the line of the Red Sea engulfing and drowning the pursuing Pharaoh's army, except all you wanted to do was call a friend and say hello. You did not want to drag Moses and his people back into bondage in Egypt.

That was not your intent, you keep telling yourself. You just wanted to make a long distance call to a friend. "Hello, Mike, how's it going? Are you happy in Cleveland?"

I have nothing but troubles with the telephone company: getting calls through, wrong billings, broken and distorted service. "Hello? Hello?" desperately whining into a void at the other end of our star system.

I even have lots of trouble getting a telephone in the first place, so that I can have all the rest of the problems. "You mean, I can't possibly have a telephone put in until the year 3009? That's ridiculous! I want to speak to your supervisor."

Then I speak to the supervisor who assures me that a mistake was made regarding the earliest installation date for a telephone being the year 3009. The supervisor promises me that I will be able to have a telephone in 2564.

"That's not soon enough. I want to talk to my friends and relatives while I'm still alive. Give me the manager!"

"Hello," the manager says, in a Saint Francis of Assisi voice.

I tell him about talking to one person who told me that I wouldn't be able to get a telephone until the year 3009, and then talking to another person who said 2564 was the earliest I could get one.

I continue ranting and raving, driven crazy by the telephone again. I tell the manager that I will have been dead for hundreds of years before the telephone is put in and that you can't talk after you're dead, and even if I could talk after I'm dead, I wouldn't have anybody to talk to because all my friends would be dead.

The manager—anyway, he says he's the manager and I have to believe him—listens sympathetically. "Yes," he says, understandingly. "I know," he says, soothing as a mint. "By the way," he says, affectionately. "Where are you calling from now?"

"A telephone booth," I say.

"It's snowing hard outside," he says, compassionately. "You must be cold and uncomfortable. This is the worst winter we've had this century."

"I am cold," I say.

By now I think I've made a new friend.

"What is the earliest I can get a telephone?" I ask, my voice calmed down by the elixir of his kindness. "I need one right now," I say. "There are people standing outside this booth who want to use the telephone. One of them has a hook for a hand and there's a young man with a tuba that has furry ants crawling all over it. I think the ants have little teeth. These people look hostile, especially an old woman who is carrying what appears to be a razor-sharp umbrella. When can I have a telephone in my house?" I plead, all self-respect long gone.

"Because you're a special case," he says, softly, "I'll put down the year 2305 and I'll make that a rush order to make sure that you get it. But if it's a decade one way or the other, don't let it bother you. When will you be home, so we can put the telephone in?"

The old woman is now circling the telephone booth with her umbrella. It looks as if it could take the head off a charging rhino with one quick stroke.

"What about the old lady?" I whisper.

"Make friends with her," he whispers. "New acquaintances can provide stimulating company. Now, when will you be home, so that we can make an appointment for your new service?"

"That's 327 years in the future," I say.

[177]

"Between 8 and 12 in the morning or 1 and 5 in the afternoon?" he continues.

"Maybe she doesn't want to be my friend," I whisper.

"I don't know why that should be," he whispers back. "You've got a marvelous personality. I already like you."

Breakfast in Beirut

This was not always my line of business. Once I travelled extensively throughout the world and my travels often took me to Beirut.

I used to love having breakfast in Beirut. There was a German restaurant near the hotel, and I would go there every morning and have breakfast: sauerbraten, red cabbage, and hot potato salad. Then I would have a double-order of Wiener schnitzel.

I would drink three bottles of beer with breakfast and finish with a piece of apple strudel and a glass of schnapps.

It is always a good idea to start the day off with a hearty German breakfast in Beirut.

Another Montana School
Gone to the Milky Way

Everything was there but the school. There were yellow signs on the road telling approaching motorists to drive carefully because there was a school nearby.

On the signs were silhouettes of a boy and a girl carrying books under their arms. The signs were designed to inspire careful driving, so that the children attending the school would grow up to be responsible citizens. Too bad there wasn't a school there.

I think of all the people who have slowed down and driven carefully but never saw the school and wondered where it was at and a lot of them probably thought that they just didn't see it, that it was their fault: How could I have missed the school?

It was very easy because the school wasn't there. I used to drive past there all the time on my way fishing up the

valley and there would be the school and children playing outside at recess or they would be inside learning how to count and who the tenth President of the United States was.

Two years ago I didn't go by there for a few weeks, maybe it was a month and when I drove past I was very eager to go fishing and didn't pay much attention to the school. I just assumed that it was there because it had been there for years and schools just don't get up and walk away.

When I drove back later that evening in the last stages of twilight, I noticed something was different as I went past the school but tricked by the hypnosis of memory and a firm belief in reality, I almost saw the school but something was different about the school and I couldn't quite figure it out.

There was something wrong with the school, I kept thinking off and on for the next few weeks, but I still couldn't figure it out. I had no reason to drive up that way, so it remained a small mystery in my life.

Then I went fishing again up that way and this time I looked very carefully at the school and it of course was gone. The school had been taken someplace and I still have no idea where, and I don't know why they moved it.

So now the signs are still there cautioning people to drive carefully because there is a school nearby. I wonder why they didn't take the signs with them when they took the school.

Maybe they forgot the signs or they didn't need them

[180]

any more, so what we have here is the case of a missing school. I hope that it's still on this planet and not taken totally away.

Four People in Their Eighties

I have been reading a book here in Tokyo about Groucho Marx. The book describes his life and wit when he was in his eighties. I read a few pages at a time. I skip around the book and lie in my hotel bed and read about Groucho Marx as an old man. Then I look out the window at a Times-Square lit section of Tokyo called Shinjuku. I have a little Groucho and a little Shinjuku. It makes an interesting balance and interlude for my life here in Tokyo.

A couple of weeks ago a Japanese poet came and had lunch with me. He was in his late forties and we talked about a great many subjects: Western movies, poetry, the difference between Japan and America, literature, Montana weather, writers that we liked and other things that interested us.

[181]

I liked the poet's intelligence. It was quick and honest. At one point I had finished saying something and then there was a pause and I could feel that he wanted to say something that was very important. He was looking at the words in his mind very carefully before he made them real by speaking.

While he paused, I waited patiently for them. He had never taken so long before to say something. I watched his mind thinking like a mystery novel with all the pages somewhere else behind a secret panel and the words hidden from me.

Then he finally spoke and what he said totally surprised me and threw me completely off balance. It was one of the most extraordinary things a person has ever said to me. I couldn't think of anything in reply and he didn't say a word more than what he had just spoken in a flat, almost confessionally-bewildered manner as if it were not quite really happening to him.

We sat there in silence for a long time, staring at each other. What he had said was this: "I live with three people over eighty years old." I searched desperately for an answer but there was none. "Interesting," was obviously not the right thing to say.

We continued staring at each other.

The time seemed endless like growing old.

My Fault

A fierce warm wind blew up from Wyoming into Montana last night and through my sleep shaking the branches of my dreams all the way down to the roots of that which I call myself.

Nightmares followed nightmares like rush hour traffic on a freeway to oblivion. I dreamt that I was a junior comedy writer on a variety show that was fading slowly from television. The Nielsen ratings loomed on the horizon like a cold, gray ax or was it just another dawn in my future?

I showed the star of the program, an ageing Jewish homosexual, an opening joke. He did not like it. "Where did you learn to write?" he said. "In a chicken house?"

The wind and the night seemed endless. My bedroom groaned like a ghost while trees continued thrashing against the sky and my dreams were shaking like a pair of false teeth in an old-folks home during an earthquake.

[183]

They jumped around in a bedside glass like a fish.

I cast off the chains of my last dream and my eyes tunnelled out of sleep at dawn. I got out of bed quickly and dressed and went outside. I wanted to escape anything that had to do with sleep.

I was greeted by all the chickens standing outside the chicken house in a blown group staring at me. They were about thirty feet away. The wind had turned the latch on the chicken house door and then it had opened the door and there were all the chickens staring at me.

Of course when a door is open, chickens have to go out and stand in the wind. That's the way chickens think. They were lucky that they were not blown away. They would have been very surprised if they had found themselves in Idaho.

The dawn and the wind were the color and movement of a gray ax. The chickens stared accusingly at me as if it were my fault that the wind was blowing so hard, that I had something to do with it and maybe even opened their God-damn door!

Florida

Sometimes it's nice to get mail here in the winter. I walk out through the snow and there are letters waiting for me in the mailbox. I take them back into the house and see what they are about.

I have a large blue mailbox like a small barn for letters. I have double-feelings about the mail: the + and − of letters. Some letters are interruptions and distractions, requesting, pleading or demanding! a piece of my life, most often from people that I have never met.

I wonder if I were to ask them as a personal favor to me not to take a bath for a week if they would do it. I don't think so, and some of the things they want me to do are just as inconvenient.

Other letters are like glasses of cold water clear as the North Star on a very hot summer afternoon. They make me feel better and renew me and I am glad that I'm alive.

[185]

Bills are forms of existential geography. They are the $
maps of where we have been.
Sometimes, frustrating.
Sometimes, pleasing.
Sometimes, nothing.
This is outrageous! I refuse to pay! or *That's fair, even
cheaper than I expected. They did good work and charged a
fair price* or *Oh, this bill for three dollars. I thought I paid
that, but I guess I didn't.*
Junk mail is just junk mail.
It passes anonymously through my hands and into the
fireplace where after a few flames it's gone. There was no
pain because there was no life.
This morning I went out to the mailbox and opened its
blue metal barn door and there was nothing for me. I
closed the door and put my hand on top of the mailbox. It
was nice and warm from the sun and felt good, almost like
being in Florida for a few seconds. We've had some cold
weather here with snow on the ground for a month.
I walked back to the house without any letters, but I felt
cheerful. Thank you, mailbox, for my little Florida vaca-
tion.

Ghosts

Sometimes just before I fall asleep I think about her, but all I can remember about her is that she had a dog. We met at a bar. We talked for a while. We had a few drinks. Then we went to her place. There was a bicycle in the front room. I almost fell over it. The bicycle was right beside the door.

We made love and she had a dog.

A Study in Thyme
and Funeral Parlors

I spend a lot of my life interested in little things, tiny portions of reality like a pinch of spice in a very complicated recipe that takes days to cook, sometimes even longer. Any more spice than the single pinch and you're walking on dangerous ground. Two pinches is totally out of the question and the meal is ruined. Send out for the hot dogs.

I'll give you an example. Last night I was walking by a funeral parlor and all the lights were out. I have never seen a funeral parlor with all the lights out at night.

It startled me.

I know that there's no federal law that says funeral parlors should keep a light on at night, but my reality assumed that's the way it should be. Obviously, I was wrong.

I thought about it as I continued on my way.

[188]

It was a little thing but it had disturbed me.

I guess nobody was home at the funeral parlor or if they were home, they didn't care to have the lights on or it didn't make any difference.

Rabbits

I have a friend who has a friend who collects rabbits in Japan. Whenever my friend travels abroad, Europe or America, she brings him back rabbits. She has brought back maybe two hundred rabbits for him. That's a lot of rabbits passing through Japanese customs even if they're not real. Her friend likes any kind of representation of a rabbit, glass or metal or a drawing or you name it as long as it has to do with rabbits.

I know nothing more about him other than he likes rabbits. I don't know how old he is or what he looks like. All I know is that a Japanese man likes rabbits.

Often, when my friend and I walk around here in Tokyo, she is half-looking for rabbits to add to his collection. If there is a little store filled with knickknacks that looks as if it could be the home of some kind of rabbit, we stop and look.

It has gotten now that when I wander around Tokyo by myself, I am sometimes half-looking for rabbits. I saw a place today that might have a rabbit and I stopped.

Who is this man?

Why rabbits?

A Different Way of Looking at President Kennedy's Assassination

Sometimes life can be a series of flea-like aggravations and pimple disappointments. You count on a simple thing happening because it has been happening for years and it's so simple and easy to do that there is no reason for it to stop happening.

It's not complicated like suddenly changing a president before his term is up or your eighty-year-old mother-in-law who gave birth to your wife when she was fifty-five, a sort of miracle birth, and she has decided to take up bowling, but she's about 4-10 and weighs 79 pounds. Her skin is stretched so tight to her tiny frail bones that she looks like a strange kite.

You know that she doesn't stand a chance in this world if she picks up a bowling ball. You make subtle hints about another activity that might be more suited to her current status in life. She nods her head and appears to be agreeing with you when you suggest knitting or stamp collecting.

Postage stamps are very exciting. When you are through talking and feeling very confident that you have persuaded her, she gives her first verbal response to your conversation.

She asks you if they have any bowling balls the size of an apple, so they might fit her fingers.

Anyway, let's forget about your eighty-year-old mother-in-law and return to the simple thing in your life that should have gone on forever without any complications. We are talking about pancakes.

A restaurant in Livingston, Montana, has been open every day, seven days a week ever since it got off Noah's Ark after The Flood, and it always serves breakfast 24 hours a day. Breakfast, of course, in Montana also means pancakes: Sourdough pancakes with lots of butter and syrup washed down with a large glass of ice-cold milk.

One night last week you couldn't sleep. You tried but it just didn't work. You went to bed at nine and wrestled

[191]

with your pillow until 2 a.m. when finally you decided to get up and go down to the restaurant and get some pancakes. An order of pancakes might make you sleep. The restaurant's only a short drive away. It's a warm night. It's not snowing. The sky is full of stars.

You park your car and go into the restaurant. You sit down at a table. There are a dozen or so people in the restaurant getting something to eat after the bars have closed. You don't need a menu.

"I'll have some pancakes and a large glass of milk," you say like a litany. The waitress doesn't ask if you also want a cup of coffee. She just points at the wall. You are a little confused and then you follow the waitress's outstretched arm to the end where her pointing finger waits. You go beyond her finger to the wall at the other end of the restaurant where there's a sign that says:

PANCAKES
WILL NOT
BE SERVED
FROM MIDNIGHT
TO 4 AM

You are stunned. This is the biggest shock to your system since President Kennedy was assassinated. You can't think of anything to say, so the waitress says it for you, looking down at her watch to make it very official, "It is now 2:30. You have to wait an hour and a half before you can get some pancakes. What would you like instead?

[192]

Ham and eggs? Bacon and eggs? Sausage and eggs? French toast?"

The word "no" stumbles out of your voice. You get up and leave the restaurant. Though the drive home is a short one it suddenly becomes a very long one like going to Billings for a funeral. You try to think of a reason why a restaurant that has served pancakes 24-hours a day since the beginning of time should suddenly change their policy and exile pancakes from their menu for four hours each day. It doesn't make any sense. How difficult is it to make pancakes?

Suddenly you think of President Kennedy.

Your eyes fill up with tears.

Portrait of a Marriage

Poor girl, she literally had nothing going for her in Tokyo. First of all, when I saw her I thought that she was a fat, ugly boy. It took about ten seconds for me to realize that she was a girl about twenty years old, maybe, because it's always so hard to tell the age of Japanese women.

My heart forgot a beat when I discovered that she was a girl. She was about 5-9 and weighed maybe 200 pounds. She was walking with somebody whose gender and appearance I have completely forgotten for when I realized that she was a girl everything else vanished into the background.

She was wearing jeans and a white T-shirt. I don't know why I'm describing her clothes. They aren't important at all, just words. I guess because I don't want to write about what I have to write next.

As she walked by, she smiled and she didn't have any front teeth. Her mouth was just a pink hole in Asia.

I know there are a lot worse fates in this world and she probably has a family and friends who love a fat girl that looks like an ugly boy and has no front teeth and she will probably find a husband who loves a girl that looks like an ugly boy with no front teeth.

Maybe he will look exactly like her and people will mistake them for twins and maybe sometimes they will make the same mistake themselves and look slightly bewildered, trying to unravel their identities, who is who.

Self-Portrait as an Old Man

Last Sunday I bought a German chocolate cake at the Methodist Church annual October auction in Pine Creek, which raised money at the auction to keep the church going for the next year.

I am not a Christian but neither is the chocolate cake. When I saw that cake, I was determined to have it. The cake was like a small three-story palace. The bidding was fast and furious and I stayed with it like a skier going down a steep slope.

"Sold to number 81 for thirty dollars!"

81 was me!

Jesus Christ! and thirty dollars for a chocolate cake!

I took it home and put it in the freezer, planning to eat it on a very special occasion like the Second Coming. I also got a receipt for the cake:

German Choc. Cake

$30.00

rec for Pine Creek Church
10/14/78

[195]

I wanted proof.

Yesterday I found myself talking to a friend about the thirty-dollar chocolate cake and then impulsively I took out my wallet and showed him the receipt for the cake.

He looked at it with an amused expression on his face.

Was this how I am going to end up? As an old man showing a barely recognizable scrap of paper to complete strangers that I have stopped and collared on the streets of the Twenty-First Century.

By this time I may have added a few totally irrelevant newspaper clippings to the chocolate cake receipt and of course I will show them off, too.

"Thirty dollars for a chocolate cake," I will chortle, pointing at a newspaper clipping that hasn't got anything to do with anything.

The Twenty-First Century inhabitant in clothes of winking green metal will humor an old man whose eyes are a little too bright.

"Thirty dollars for a chocolate cake," I will rattle again from my reed-dry scrawny throat.

"That's very interesting," the inhabitant will say but will really be wondering if I had just been sprung from a living time capsule, meanwhile thinking, *"I guess this old man has not bought a cup of coffee recently because that costs fifty dollars, and five dollars extra if you want cream and sugar."*

"Thirty dollars!" and my world only a memory . . . one afternoon at the Pine Creek Methodist Church back in the Twentieth Century.

[196]

Beer Story

"I like to cook in the winter," the sixty-year-old Italian cook said, somewhere in California, holding his glass of beer in a professional grip. He was a man who totally knew the meaning of beer. Beer was an open book to him. He knew every page of beer by heart.

"I like to cook in the winter," he repeated. "It's just right, then. In the summer it's too hot, too hot. I should know. I've been cooking for forty-two years. It's never any different. The only good thing about cooking in the summer is that I drink more beer, but I do that anyway, so I might as well drink it in the winter when it's not so hot and I can enjoy myself more."

He took another sip of beer.

"After people get to know me, they all say I drink a lot of beer. I don't deny it either. Why should I? I'm not ashamed of beer."

Homage to Rudi Gernreich / 1965

The look in clothes expresses an anti-attitude, the result of being bored . . . And so, if you're bored, you go for the outrageous gesture. Everything else seems to have lost any meaning.

—RUDI GERNREICH

Beneath the freeway that joins San Francisco to the Golden Gate Bridge, like lovers to a marriage, is a small cemetery surrounded by a white picket fence so short that you can step over it, and the graves are only a few feet long.

The cars that pass over the freeway are translated into a gentle *clang, clang, clang* below in the cemetery where the wind blows among the flowers and the weeds. It is a sound that never stops all the time that you are there.

You can look straight up and see nothing but the red meat-like metal of the freeway and the gray concrete that carries the freeway up to the cars.

[198]

This cemetery is but a gnat compared to the cemetery further up the hill in the Presidio of San Francisco where thousands of graves climb in military precision and conformity. These graves are punctuated with small white tombstones that are out on patrol in eternity.

I could never be this cemetery with its glory like slices of bread in a star-spangled loaf, and the American flag towering like a huge baker above the graves. But I could quite easily become the little cemetery down below the freeway where the soldiers bury their pets.

I could put on its graves and markers and flowers like a Rudi Gernreich coat and stay there for a few hours idly dreaming in the windy California sun.

I like the general informality of the pet cemetery. It suits me with the audacity of its affection. I seem to find almost more love here than in the cemetery up the hill.

It's ironic that I should spend a Sunday afternoon with dead military pets while our armies are in the Dominican Republic and South Vietnam and all my friends are worried silly about it.

To arrive at the pet cemetery I had to pass through the fort, and drive past barracks and soldiers and green military equipment and cannons parked in a plaza.

The Presidio is the home of the 6th Army, and soon I was standing in the pet cemetery, listening to the *clang, clang, clang* of the cars above on the freeway while I surveyed the dead pets of the 6th Army.

I walked among the graves and there were many frail dandelions growing in the sandy soil of the cemetery and little purple flowers and little white flowers, fragile like miniature chandeliers.

There were dogs buried there: Smudge, Butch, Shorty Johnson, Satan, Hula-Girl, Caesar, Sally, Wimpy, Tony McGuire, a fishing pal, and Oscar E945, a sentry dog.

There were cats buried there: Blackout, Cutie, Regina, and Patches who was born in Dachau.

There was a hamster: Willie.

And a pigeon: Deed.

And two parakeets: Jingle and Peppi.

There were two goldfish: Peter and Lela "God bless them both."

And there was Tweeter whose epitaph read:

HERE LIES TWEETER
WRAPPED IN SILK
THE LITTLE BIRD
DROWNED IN A
GLASS OF MILK

There were many fine graves and many minor graves and as I read the epitaphs of dogs, I could hear dogs barking in the Presidio, pets that were still on duty.

One grave had a pile of carefully selected rocks on it and a plastic Madonna lying on her side with her face turned toward the gravemarker of a silenced pet.

Another grave was just a plain stake stuck in the ground and stapled to the stake was an old nameless piece of paper, looking almost like the sky in a Japanese painting. There were three rusty bottle caps lying beneath it, and the rust had taken their identities away. They were nameless as the pet buried there.

Around one grave there was a white fence uprooted and crooked with a heart or an apple drawn on one of the pickets and the word LOVE was written in the center of the heart or the apple.

Beside another grave I found a pacified mole, looking like a dead seal with a Pinocchio nose, and at the other end of the cemetery I found an empty package of Force's Gopher Killer. It had been a case of mistaken identity, but nevertheless very effective. It seemed strange to me that death should be practiced as an active force in a sanctuary of death, but perhaps it was only the day and the way the Rudi Gernreich coat fit. I'll have to admit the graves were a little tight across the shoulders.

I found the inevitable potter's field where dead pets lay almost anonymously in the ground and the weeds and the flowers hardly dared to grow.

And I saw grand graves covered with fine white rocks and there were marble tombstones and wax flowers and some of them even had flowers and plants and cactuses growing on the graves in white boxes.

Somebody driving by in their car upon the freeway had thrown their empty April to May 1965 Golden Gate Bridge commuter ticket book out of the car window and it had landed on the grave of Penny, a ten-year-dead pet.

One gravemarker had a yellow sun painted child-like on it with the rays of the sun shining down the marker toward the ground.

There was a white marker for a pet named Checkers that said very starkly: "It was done."

At another place in the cemetery I saw the all too familiar signature of the good old American necrophilic beerdrinker. There was an empty Olympia beer can lying beside some markers that had been knocked down.

I have never been able to understand why people want to go to the store and buy some beer and then immediately head for the nearest cemetery to drink the beer and knock down gravemarkers.

I wonder if it has anything to do with the American mother abandoning breast-feeding her young. Perhaps as a culture we are not quite ready for the bottle yet.

I don't know how long I had been in the cemetery when I looked up beyond the grave of a dog to see two soldiers coming down the hill.

They had rifles slung over their shoulders and they were carrying mess kits in their hands. I knew the pet cemetery was not a restricted area, so I gave their approach only a passing glance and went back to looking at the dog's grave.

I looked up again to see that the soldiers were very close and that one of them had handed his mess kit to the other soldier and then had taken the rifle off his shoulder and was advancing toward me with the rifle in his hands.

Suddenly he jumped forward and landed on both feet in front of me, balanced on the balls of his feet. He held the rifle across his chest with both of his hands.

He was standing outside the cemetery and I was standing inside the cemetery.

[202]

"Halt! Who goes there?" he yelled, looking sternly at me with his finger on the trigger of the rifle. I was surrounded by hundreds of dead dogs and cats and goldfish and hamsters and pigeons and parakeets and Tweeter who had the misfortune of drowning in a glass of milk.

"It's all right for me to be here," I said gently, appreciating fully "the outrageous gesture," and told him that I had gotten permission from the provost marshal.

"What are you doing?" he said, still holding the gun in position across his chest.

"I'm writing a little story about this cemetery," I said. He smiled and relaxed his rifle. "Well, put me in your story," he said.

I looked at his mess kit and said, "Are you going to lunch?"

"No," he said. "We've already had lunch. We're going to South Vietnam."

He and the other soldier were smiling and laughing to each other as they walked away. I think they thought up this "Halt! Who goes there?" pet cemetery business as a kind of joke to attack the boredom of a Sunday afternoon. They looked awfully young to be soldiers. They no doubt would be older when they came back from South Vietnam.

As for me, I soon departed: leaving behind the Rudi Gernreich coat draped over that short white fence beneath the freeway. It seemed to belong there.

Turkey and Dry
Breakfast Cereal Sonata

The turkeys got into a knockdown drag out battle with
no holds barred. They were really going at it and the two
ponies just got bored with it all and galloped out of the
woods into an open field, leaving the turkeys to sort out
their own domestic problems.

I had walked a quarter of a mile down to the lodge
which was closed and I knew it was closed before I started
out. I just wanted to check the blue sign in the front door
window again.

I of course already knew what it said, but I just wanted
to check it out again because I had nothing else to justify
walking down there for, and I wanted to take a morning
walk, so I used reading the sign again as an excuse and
walked through the very quiet and still little community of
Pine Creek.

It was a good walk, my footsteps crunching fresh snow that sounded like expensive breakfast cereal as I stepped on it, almost like music from General Mills.

The blue sign was still there on the door and its message had not changed. It still said thank you for patronage and friendship from the old owners and that the store would stay closed until February 20th when the new owners would take over, and that they looked forward to meeting everybody.

I wondered how much and what kind of change the lodge would make under new ownership. I thought about the new owners and what kind of people they were to run a small lodge which included one gas pump, a little café-store combination and a few log cabins in barely a spot on the map: Pine Creek, Montana, so far from Paris, New York or Tokyo.

I would find out about the new directions, if any, in the lodge and meet the new owners in a few days. So far, nothing had changed with the lodge and nobody was there.

The new ownership of the lodge was a small mystery that would keep me interested for a few days, something to think about here in the Montana winter.

Then the turkeys started fighting in the woods across the road from the lodge and the ponies ran out of the woods into a field and I turned around and walked back home, listening to the sound of breakfast cereal under my feet.

Old Man Working the Rain

Every day I see people in Tokyo handing out handbills to other people. This is the way they make their living, by standing on the street handing out handbills to total strangers, wanting them to spend their money on something they may or may not need.

Most of the time the strangers don't make use of the handbills. They just throw them away and forget about them.

I also see men holding signs that want other men to spend their money in nearby massage parlors and cabarets where there are women for the purposes that men use women and that women get money for.

Often the men are old and wear poor sloppy clothes, standing there holding erotically promising signs. I wish the old men were not doing that. I wish they were doing something else and their clothes looked better.

But I can't change the world.

[206]

It was already changed before I got here.

Sometimes when I finish writing something, perhaps even this, I feel as if I am handing out useless handbills or I am an old man standing in the rain, wearing shitty clothes and holding a sign for a cabaret that is filled with the beautiful and enticing skeletons of young women that sound like dominoes when they walk toward you coming in the door.

The Remarkable Dining Cars
of the Northern Pacific Railroad

"The remarkable dining cars of the Northern Pacific Railroad used to feature two great products of the Northwest in the days when railroads catered to the public."

That is the first sentence of a recipe for baked apples in a cookbook called *American Cookery* by James Beard. It is a very good recipe and reading it started my mind to dreaming like a small airplane taking off from a rural airfield on a cold December morning.

The plane, my dreams, slowly circles the airfield gaining altitude and then the course is set. It is lined up perfectly on my compass:

a baked apple is my destination.

That's where I'm going at a comfortable speed of 150 miles an hour over fields and orchards of late autumn with smoke curling up like apple peelings from the chimneys of farm houses.

It's easy to see that I love baked apples hot and fresh from the oven with rich cream poured like the wings of an angel over them. The first bite makes my taste buds seem like the Grand Canyon filled to the rim with pleasure.

The flight is over.

My airplane just made a perfect landing on a baked apple.

Railroading in Tokyo

As a child I listened to "Chattanooga Choo-Choo" when it was a brand-new song, an infant song. Now it is middle-aged and the song's hair is starting to turn gray. I never listened to all the words. I listened to just snatches of them and probably sang those snatches or maybe just sang the words:

"track 29"

and let it go at that. Now so many years later with it just starting to rain at a little sidewalk café in Tokyo, "Chattanooga Choo-Choo" was played over the sound system and I listened to all the words, the entire song for the first time as if the words were lumber and a house was being built out of them. When the song was finished, the house was built and there it was in my mind on a little side street near the river.

I marvelled at the fact that it had taken me so many years to listen to all the words of "Chattanooga Choo-Choo." Then I heard my own voice singing softly in the Tokyo afternoon just beginning to rain:

"track 29."

Two Montana Humidifiers

There's very little humidity up here in the wintery mountains of Montana. I remember somebody once told me that this place is geologically classified as a high alpine desert, though I don't think in those terms because we have rivers filled with trout and there are beautiful forests here.

I'm living in the mountains is the way I look at it.

Anyway, we have a foot of snow on the ground and the air is very dry. We've been getting our humidity in the house by leaving a pan of water on the stove under a low heat. A few days ago I decided that we needed a humidifier.

Why not?

Let's breathe some air with a little moisture in it. I'd never bought a humidifier before. It would be an interesting experience. Yes, you can teach an old dog new tricks. Let him buy a humidifier and find out what it's about. I had no idea how they even worked.

I was a little excited by the prospect as my wife and I drove into town through seemingly endless snow.

We parked the car and made our way carefully across the icy sidewalk and into a hardware variety-type store, which certainly had to be the dwelling place of a humidifier.

A young woman was holding a child in her arms and there was a young man standing beside her who was also holding a child in his arms.

One of the children was a year old and the other one was a baby, just a few months old. Their parents were trying to make up their minds to buy something that required very serious expressions on their faces.

They were standing beside the cash register where a clerk was patiently waiting for them to make up their minds. The clerk was trying to help them out, so she also had a very serious expression on her face.

Fortunately, my mind was already made up, so I said to the clerk, "Excuse me, I'd like to buy a humidifier."

"They're over there," she said, pointing at something which had to be a humidifier, though I couldn't be certain because I'd never seen one before.

I walked over to where she had pointed and looked down at a humidifier. I don't know what I had expected but it wasn't really that exciting. It was a brown metal cabinet with a ventilated plastic grill on top.

Encountering a humidifier for the first time certainly did not rank as one of the great experiences of my life. I had no idea how it worked.

[211]

"How does this thing work?" I asked the clerk. She was standing about thirty feet away with the very serious young couple who were still trying to make up their minds.

"What do you think?" the young mother said.

"I don't know," the young father said.

"It's on sale," the clerk said.

"Excuse me," I said, walking back to the clerk. "If you're not too busy, could you show me how the humidifier works?"

I could see that the young couple still had some more thinking to do. They weren't going anyplace. They were rooted in their tracks. The children were being very good, so they could think about what they wanted to buy without being interrupted. The babies were aimlessly looking around. They had no idea where they were at.

"You're interested in buying a humidifier?" the clerk said.

"Yes," I said.

"Well, let's go look at it," she said and started around the counter.

Just then the young mother turned to the young father—they were both about twenty years old, just kids themselves—and said, "That's one thing we don't have to get. A humidifier. We've got two of them right here," gesturing toward the babies and their diapers.

We all laughed.

And then the young people went back to serious thinking about buying something that will always remain a mystery to me because when I left the store with my humidi-

[212]

fier, they were still standing at the counter trying to make
up their minds.

Contents for Good Luck

I read a beautiful and very sad poem today by the Japanese poet Shuntaro Tanikawa about the unfaithfulness of
women and how hard it is to sleep with them that first
night after you know they have been with another man
that day. They always fall asleep and you lie there beside
them wide awake, feeling a tremendous loneliness created
by the touch of their sleeping body. They are warm with
the sperm of another man inside of them like a stove but
you are very cold, so cold that you feel as if you had been
hatched from a penguin egg in Antarctica and died
shortly afterwards becoming a thumbful of frozen feathers
on a continent where there is not a single post office and
the only mail delivery is the wind.

She turns over in her sleep, puts her arm around you
and her touch is the cold wind of Antarctica bringing you

your mail and blowing your heart into mirror-like shadows of darkness.

You of course will go on loving her, but it will be a different kind of love. It will never be as it was before and you will start tomorrow. As you lie there waiting for the dawn, you are sharing the company of men since the beginning of time.

In the dark shadows of the bedroom, you see another bed with a Roman soldier lying in it beside his wife who is sleeping soundly. He is staring at the ceiling waiting for the dawn which will stretch slowly across the sky like a defeated sword, bringing no comfort.

It is an old story.

In the dark shadows of his bed is an Egyptian bed three thousand years before Christ where the woman is sleeping happily and the man stares at the ceiling, and in the dark just beyond the Egyptian's bed are caves and animal skin beds.

The awake man or creature resembling man stares at the ceiling of the cave. His woman or creature that resembles woman snores happily unaware what he is thinking in whatever mental symbols mean something to him.

I could kill her or just forget about it. Try and live with it. Why did she do it? Now I will have to start loving her in a completely different way. The old way is gone.

Tod

For the first time in eight days the temperature is over thirty degrees, so it's a good time to examine games and what they've had to do with my life and why I don't play them any more.

I don't read the funnies in the newspaper any more either but that's a different story and will be gone into at a later time.

. . . much later.

Let's get back to games:

When I was a child I liked games. They were a good way to pass a rainy day. I played Parcheesi, Monopoly, Authors and Old Maid. Monopoly was my favorite game and also checkers had their share of rainy days.

As childhood slowly went away, so did the games. They are forgotten or stored in an attic someplace. Perhaps in a house that no one lives in any more on a street that's hard to find where the house numbers don't quite make sense. The 2's look like 7's and the 5's look like 1's.

In my early twenties I played lots of chess and in my early thirties I played a lot of dominoes. I stopped playing chess when I was twenty-five and dominoes went when I was thirty-three. Why? I just got tired of them and stopped. It's that simple.

From time to time every few years, I've played a little poker but not much because I don't have any luck. I always lose, so it's really not any fun. Who likes to lose all the time and that's what I do when I play poker.

So this gets us up to last night and a game of Scrabble in a house surrounded by snow in the deep Montana winter.

The game was not my idea.

I have never never played Scrabble and did not have the slightest interest in it or knew what it was about except that it was some kind of word game. You made up words with letters on little wooden blocks.

I cannot think of anything more boring because what are you going to do with the words after you've made them up? You might as well try breathing into a vacuum cleaner for fun.

Anyway, a visiting friend bought the game at a store in town and I knew that sooner or later the game would be played and somehow I would be dragged into it. I hoped later but of course it turned out to be sooner, and I found myself at a table with a board in front of me demanding that words be made up and I had seven little wooden blocks with letters on them to oblige the board.

I felt silly as the game started.

First of all, I'm not a very good speller and it didn't

make much sense for me to play a game that depended on spelling for victory.

The person who bought the game is of course a very good speller, a speller of almost championship ability. I can see why he liked and wanted to play the game, but I couldn't see what there was ultimately in it for me, except the annoyance of wasting my time losing.

There were four of us and the game started.

Right from the very beginning when I selected my seven blocks of wood, I didn't like the game and within a few moments dislike turned to true hatred. I've never hated anything so fast in my life.

Among the first words played on the board was the word quieten as in quieten down, which I found to be an absurd word. Here in the West we use quiet down, not quieten down. I had never even heard the word quieten before, so I made a big mistake by compulsively looking it up in the dictionary, and there it was in all its glory: quieten, an English word, a word used in England. I don't know English English. I know American English.

That's enough for me.

It serves the purposes of my life.

The next word played was ted. I'd never even heard of the word ted before. I'd of course heard of teddy bear and the name Ted, but not ted as a word. It was contributed by my friend who is a good speller. Again impetuously I went to the dictionary like a pig to bacon and God-damn it! there was the word ted.

If you want to find out what the word means look it up

[217]

yourself or if you already know what it means, that's your problem, but I'd like to hear you use it in conversation sometime: "Please ted the cow shit or I have tedded the grass. What else do you want me to do?"

Yeah, go right ahead and use that word.

I dare you!

That gets us around to the next word that was played after ted. Right after ted came tod. There it was: tod, looking up at me from the board, not a name or related to a hot toddy but something completely different: tod, as in, "Look, a tod!" Try that on your friends the next time you see a fox or try crafty as a tod and see how much response you get to that.

Tod is a Scottish word for fox.

I immediately escaped from the game.

I was a prisoner of war who made a brilliant escape from a prison camp belonging to the silly forces of Scrabble.

There was a big stirring at my departure and much coaxing was done trying to get me back into the game, but I was firm in my resolve. I got up laughing from the table and went and sat on the couch.

As they tried to coax me back to the table and the game, I sat on the couch laughing.

"Look," I said. "There's a tod in the chicken house. My, what a beautiful tod coat. Where did you get it? In the dictionary. Well, it certainly looks good on you."

Five Ice-Cream Cones
Running in Tokyo

For Rubin Glickman

Normally, if you were to think about an ice-cream cone running, you'd think of it dripping and you have to keep licking fiercely away, like an anteater, to keep it from getting on you instead of in you.

When you are dealing with the absolute reality of ice-cream cones, the word *in* is very positive, preferred, and the word *on* is negative. You don't need it.

I just saw a Japanese family: father, mother and their three little children running up the street, carrying in their hands ice-cream cones.

Somehow I consider this a small miracle. I have never seen an entire family running up the street with ice-cream cones. They were all very happy. Maybe this is a new definition of running.

The Good Work of Chickens

The sweet turbines of revenge purred gently in his mind like the voice of a beautiful woman and relaxed him to the point that it didn't feel strange or even out of the ordinary for him to be driving a dump truck full of chicken shit down a quiet street with his lights out in a prosperous middle-class residential neighborhood.

He had bought the truckload of chicken shit earlier that day at a huge chicken ranch in White Sulphur Springs, Montana, and had driven it to the town of View, Montana, a distance of over two hundred miles.

He had never done anything like this before and he enjoyed the whole procedure of borrowing a friend's dump truck and driving it to White Sulphur Springs to buy the chicken shit and watching it being loaded onto the truck.

"This sure is a lot of chicken shit," one of the men said who was helping load the truck.

[220]

"Yes," said the proud new owner of the chicken shit. "It is a lot, isn't it?"

"What are you going to do with all this shit?" the man asked who liked to talk with people because he spent so much time with chickens.

"I'm going to make sure that it gets to the right place."

"Well," the chicken shit loader said, for lack of anything better to say. "I hope this chicken shit works out for the best."

"It will," the man said, who we'll call Mike, though his name was C. Edwin Jackson because his right name is not important. It's what he did with that chicken shit that's important.

Mike drove slowly almost anonymously past house after house in the early evening of a cold February night, looking for the right house. He had muddied up the license plates of the truck, so that it would be hard to trace.

That's how he had gotten the address of his destination, a house on Butte Street, by tracing the owner's license plate number when their car drove away leaving a bewildered little dog in its wake.

The people in the car had abandoned the dog in the country near his place. When he saw what the people were doing, he ran out of the house but it was too late to stop them. He yelled at them but they drove away ignoring him and leaving the little dog standing there frightened in the road as its masters drove off, abandoning it to the cruel fates of the Montana countryside.

Mike thought about getting his shotgun and pursuing

[221]

them, but then he memorized their license plate number and went into the house and wrote it down right away because he had decided to put into operation a revenge fantasy that he had courted in his mind like a beautiful woman for years now.

He had a small ranch out in the country about ten miles from the small town of View and people were always driving out and dumping their unwanted animals on his property. Poor dogs and cats doomed to the shock of abandonment, *farewell, nice home,* and to the agonies of starvation and survival in a world where they could not survive.

One minute they were happy domestic pets and as soon as they were put outside the car or truck, they were just another wretched creature doomed to a slow and agonizing death.

Domestic animals cannot survive by themselves in this country. They suffer minute to minute, hour to hour, day to day until kind Death touches their lives with the shadow of his life.

Country people don't want these animals. They already have their own animals. Why do people think that strangers will take care of their animals after they no longer want to take care of them themselves?

There simply is not room for a hundred cats and fifty dogs at every house in the country. People at the most have a few dogs or cats and that's about it.

There truly is no room at the inn.

It's full.

Anyway, Mike or C. Edwin Jackson had had it up to his

ears with the cruelty of people abandoning their pets in the country to die a slow and painful death.

He had seen puppies starved down so much that they looked like the shadows of string with no other response to life than hunger like bowling going on in their stomachs.

He once saw a kitten eating an ear of corn in the garden and he had seen a cat standing in a creek, the water was a very cold six-inches deep, trying to catch a fish.

Hunger had driven a house cat to become a fisherman.

Yes, he had no love in his heart for people who would do things like that to animals and he had slowly evolved this fantasy of revenge upon those who abandoned the helpless without even the mercy to take their unwanted animals to the veterinarian and let him painlessly take care of the business, so that no suffering would occur. Sometimes he thought that people abandoned their animals just to save the few dollars that the vet would cost.

Mike tried to think of what those people thought about when they took their animals away from their homes and drove them out to the horror of trying to stay alive in the country.

But now there was going to be an element of fairness introduced into it and he was only a few blocks away from 14 Butte Street and the beauty of his revenge.

It was a quiet house, large and spacious and occupied by a middle-aged man and his wife and their conveniently-absent dog.

"Have you found your dog yet?" one of their neighbors asked the day after it had "disappeared."

[223]

"No, Little Scott is still missing."

"Well, we hope you find him. He's such a cute dog."

"So do we. We love that dog."

"Don't worry. You'll find him."

The man and woman were watching *The Six Million Dollar Man* on television when Mike backed the truck up over the curb and across their lawn to the front porch and dumped three tons of chicken shit on it.

The man jumped up from the television set. He jumped up so fast that you'd think he was the Six Million Dollar Man.

The woman screamed.

She didn't know it yet but she was going to have to cancel her appointment at the beauty parlor tomorrow. She would be doing something else.

The weight of the chicken shit forced the front door open and it poured into their living room like an avalanche.

Three tons of chicken shit is a lot of dedicated chickens and their work had not been in vain.

Castle of the Snow Bride

. . . what is missing here is much more important than what follows because what is absent is the ending of a Japanese erotic movie called *Castle of the Snow Bride*. It was a fantastically sensual film. After watching just a few scenes I had an erection that was like that of a teenage boy. It was hot and unstable, shimmering like heat in the desert.

The actresses in the movie were the ultimate in beauty, grace and pleasure. They were doing things that became gradually more and more complicated and more and more imaginative.

The pressure of my erection had reached the point of almost throwing me backwards, right out of my seat into the lap of the person sitting behind me.

My body was dizzy with sex like a maelstrom in a tropical sea and my mind came and went like the continuous slamming of a hot door.

The movie progressed deeper and deeper into more complicated and phantasmagorical sex, travelling toward the most sensual experience I had ever seen or imagined. It was going to make all my previous sexual experience seem as if I had spent my life working as a bookkeeper for a small brick and mousetrap company in a town so bleak and boring that it didn't even have a name. The people who lived there had kept putting off naming the town for over a hundred years.

"We'll have to name this town next year," was the way they kept handling it and that's exactly how my sex life would compare to the way the movie was going to end.

There were nine minutes left before the picture ended. I remembered that from the program in the box office window. The movie was going to end at 7:09 and the clock on the theater wall said 7:00. In less than ten minutes my sex life was going to be totally obsolete, a thing of the past.

The female erotic goings on in front of me were now starting to turn the seats in the theater into steam. It was an interesting experience and pleasurable feeling my seat being vaporized by sensuality.

Then something happened that caused me to get up and go out into the lobby. It was an errand of incredible importance. It had to be done. It could not be avoided. There things got kind of complicated because they are not clear.

I may have gotten up to get a drink of cold pop because I thought I had enough time to buy one and get back into the theater before the final sexual scene or it may have

[226]

been something different that drew me out of the theater.

Perhaps I had to go to the toilet or maybe I had to give somebody a very important letter and we had agreed to meet in the lobby of the theater and I had no idea when the movie started that it was going to reveal the most fantastic sexual scene of all time.

Anyway, I did what I was supposed to do in the lobby, whatever that was, and rushed back into the theater to see the curtain close on the end of the movie that was a long shot of a castle at sunset with crows circling it.

The lights went on for the intermission and the theater was filled with unconscious men. Some of them were lying in the aisles. All the men had expressions of bliss on their faces as if the Angel of Pleasure had touched them while I was doing whatever I was doing.

It was the last showing of the movie that night, but fortunately the film would be shown for one more day. I went home in a state of frustrated hell on earth. The night passed like ice-cold water dripping a drop at a time on a burning erection that lasted all through my sleep, trapping me in a state of considerable pain.

The program said that the first showing of *Castle of the Snow Bride* was at 12:01 p.m. The morning passed like a monkey trying to dance in a block of ice.

When I went to the theater at a quarter of twelve, it had disappeared. There was no trace of it. In its place was a small park with children playing and old people sitting on benches reading.

I tried to ask people about the theater but nobody spoke

[227]

English. When I finally found somebody who could speak English, he told me apologetically that he was just a tourist from Osaka, visiting Tokyo for the first time and he knew nothing about the theater, but the park was beautiful. He liked the way it looked because it had so many trees.

Later I met some people who had a good knowledge of Japanese movies. I asked them about *Castle of the Snow Bride*. They had never heard of it and was I certain that was the right title?

Yes, I was certain. There could only be one *Castle of the Snow Bride*. They were sorry that they could not help me. So there you have it: Everything is here except that which is missing.

The Instant Ghost Town

Here are just a few quick words from Montana before going into town because somebody has to go to town today. If everybody stayed home, the town would be empty. There would be no traffic and the streets would be abandoned and all the stores would be haunted by an absence of people on a holidayless Wednesday. It might be on the 6 o'clock national news. It would be presented as a joke for everyone to laugh at:

"Today in Livingston, Montana, population 7000, all the folks decided to stay home, so the town became a ghost town for 24 hours. No official reason has yet been given for this unique event. The mayor had no comment when contacted by ABC News late this afternoon, so we can go on safely assuming that Montana is still the last frontier."

The anchorman would finish the joke with a big anchor smile on his face like the anchor of the *Titanic* settling to the bottom.

Nobody out here wants that to happen, so I have to go to town and make myself highly visible. I hope that everyone will follow my example. I don't want my absence to contribute to an instant ghost town.

The Mouse

Sitting down at a table at the same sidewalk café in Tokyo, I smelled something dead. I looked around but I couldn't see anything dead and then the smell went away, so I ordered some coffee.

Before the coffee arrived, the smell of something dead came back but vanished in just a few seconds. Then I was drinking coffee. The next time the smell of something dead came, I of course paid attention to it, but I didn't let it bother me.

The wind was blowing and I thought maybe it came on the wind, so I let it be, and very carefully watched people coming and going in the street. I love to watch people and Japan is a good place for it. I sat there for hours watching people and after I finished with the coffee, I drank a little wine.

The smell came and went a hundred times and after a while it didn't bother me because I knew that it would go away. It smelled like vinegar turning to sugar and sugar turning to vinegar. What I smelled was the middle point of their passage. In other words, the smell of death was on the wind or so I thought until I discovered that it was not the wind that brought the smell, but it was I who brought it. Every time I lowered my head toward my chest the smell came. Then I realized that it was coming from my own heart.

There was something dead in my heart.

I tried to figure out what it was by the strength of the smell. I knew that it was not a lion or a sheep or a dog. Using logical deduction, I came to the conclusion that it was a mouse.

I had a dead mouse in my heart.

What was I to do?

I was trying to figure that out when a beautiful Japanese woman sat down at the table next to me. Her table was very close and she was wearing a delicate but dominating perfume, like death in another direction, and the smell of her perfume made it possible for me not to smell the dead mouse in my heart any more.

She is sitting next to me right now. I wish I could tell her what I just told you about the mouse and her perfume, but I don't think she would understand.

As long as she sits here, everything will be all right.

I have to figure out what to do next.

[231]

House of Carpets

An electric sign in a snowstorm town is flashing HOUSE OF CARPETS on and off: HOUSE OF CARPETS off and on. It's a November night in Montana and the streets are abandoned. Everybody wants to get away from the snowstorm. There is only a very occasional car, rare like an old postage stamp. The snow swirls about the sign that wants people to buy carpets from a closed store.

The carpets are inside but the door is locked and the carpet people have gone home.

I cannot figure out why they have a flashing sign on at night when there's nobody there to sell carpets. If you were walking along and saw the sign, say at midnight, and it excited you enough to want to buy a carpet, you couldn't buy one because the HOUSE OF CARPETS is closed.

On a snowy, damned-cold night like this one, seeing that sign, you might want to buy a carpet to roll up in and keep warm.

But forget about it.

[232]

The 1977 Television Season

Last night the temperature went down to 12 degrees. It was our coldest night of the autumn. I kept checking the temperature while watching television: situation comedies, etc.

I followed the temperature faithfully like an ice-cube shepherd hour after hour going down from 30 to 12 degrees. I would watch some television and then go outside on the back porch and check the temperature.

This is a hard thing to say about American popular culture and I'm weighing my words very carefully but the temperature was much more interesting than television.

Too bad the temperature couldn't have been a program. Then I wouldn't have had to get up and go outside to check it. I could have just sat there and the 9 o'clock program would have been 16 degrees Fahrenheit.

The Window

    —like a kitchen window steaming up on a very cold morning and it's hard to see out of, then the steam slowly disappears and you can see the snow-covered mountains, 10,000 feet high, out the window, and then the window gradually steams up again, coffee on the stove and the mountains gone like a dream.

    . . . that's how I feel this morning.

Painstaking Popcorn Label

The night before last it seemed like a wonderful idea to stay up until 3 o'clock in the morning drinking one bottle of sour mash whiskey and putting a dent in a second bottle. Yesterday afternoon the shortcomings of that idea revealed themselves in the form of an almost morbid hangover and I found myself sitting at the kitchen table desperately reading the label on an empty jar of popcorn.

The label told me more about the former contents of the jar than I ever wanted to know about popcorn. I just like to pop some corn from time to time, maybe once a month is enough, but this label totally ignored my simple approach to popcorn. It went into great detail about the man who grew the popcorn and his growing of it. It mentioned thousands of "painstaking" experiments and forty generations of fancy seed-breeding to arrive at his brand of "gourmet" popcorn. It mentioned "tender care" and protection from "alien pollination" and used the words "technical" and "scientific" and referred to their product as popping corn instead of popcorn. It also used the phrase "unspeakably ordinary" corns. I was surprised that they did not use the word general when talking about their corn.

Anyway, my head hurt and I didn't want to know all that shit about the farmer and his "popping corn." The jar was empty. I couldn't get any pleasure or diversion out of popping his corn, which of course would have been impossible even if I'd had some. My brain was too morbid to handle a pan full of howling corn.

After I finished reading the label I vowed never to buy any of that popcorn again.

There's just so much room for so much information here in the Twentieth Century and you have to draw the line someplace and I was drawing it the next time I bought some popcorn. It would just be a simple bag of popcorn and not have the word painstaking printed on it.

Imaginary Beginning to Japan

This is the beginning of an imaginary first trip to Japan. You get on the airplane in San Francisco. You are very excited. Japan! The trip has taken months of planning. You have gotten your first passport, a smallpox shot and you have read tourist books about Japan and Japanese customs. You practice simple Japanese words and phrases: "O hayō" means good morning.

The day of departure grows closer. You have promised to bring back presents, teapots and fans, etc. You have promised to write thousands of postcards. You start packing two weeks early. You don't want to forget anything. You buy your traveler's checks and get your airplane ticket.

Then comes the big day and you are flying across the Pacific to Japan. The hours pass. Your excitement is almost out of control: A country thousands of years old, a civilization that was building great temples before the Americans were even building chicken houses!

You don't see anything for ten hours and then you see the coast and beginning at the shore's edge Japan!

As the airplane gets closer and closer to the coast, you can see millions of people standing on the beaches. Their faces are looking skyward in the direction of your airplane and closer and closer you fly until you can tell that the people are all looking up at your airplane and they have something in their hands that they are starting to wave at the airplane.

At first you can't make out what they are waving at the plane and then suddenly, like a miracle, you can see what it is. Millions of Japanese men, women and children are waving their chopsticks at the airplane.

Welcome to Japan!

Leaves

I have been so totally erased from nature lately, like a blackboard before school starts, that yesterday when I was in the Japanese section of San Francisco: Japantown, I saw the sidewalk littered with chocolate wrappers.

There were hundreds of them. Who in the hell has been eating all these chocolates? I thought. A convention of Japanese chocolate eaters must have passed this way.

Then I noticed some plum trees on the street. Then I noticed that it was autumn. Then I noticed that the leaves were falling as they will and as they must every year.

Where had I gone wrong?

Waking Up Again

I feel as if I have the weight of the world on my shoulders. In my scale of concern and detail Atlas would only come up to my knees and his world would be the size of a basketball.

My mind is racing forward at such a speed that compared to it, a bolt of lightning would seem like an ice cube in an old woman's forlorn glass of weak lemonade on some front porch lost in Louisiana. She stares straight ahead at nothing, holding the glass of lemonade in her hand.

In other words: My sense of mental geography is a little more than a bit off. Actually, I'm about halfway to Albuquerque. I took a wrong turn when I opened my eyes this morning and the second wrong turn when I got out of bed.

Where I would like to be is where I'm at, but now I find myself on Route 66, fifty miles from Albuquerque with the shadow of San Francisco in the background like a paralyzed film dissolve.

Then suddenly the dissolve implodes like a television set dying of a heart attack, New Mexico vanishes, and I'm instantly returned to San Francisco where I've been all the time and for the last minute walking down the Kearny Street Stairs toward Broadway.

What has brought all this about is the total reality of a window filled with drying duckbills and chicken feet. The rest of the birds are gone, only bills and feet remain.

It is an apartment window that I think probably belongs to a Chinese person and they have five strings of duckbills and chicken feet hanging outside the window drying in the sun. I don't know what they are used for, perhaps a special once-in-a-hundred-years Chinese feast or maybe just ordinary soup. Eat it when you're hungry.

All I know is that their reality has reestablished mine and I am starting the day all over again on the Kearny Street Stairs as if I had just awakened.

Poetry Will Come
to Montana on March 24th

That's what it says in *TV Guide*.

Poetry will be here at 6 o'clock in the morning on Friday. I look forward to poetry coming here to this land of cows and mountains. It will arrive just after the *Early Farm Watch* and be in Montana for half an hour until 6:30 before going on to its next appointment. Perhaps Arizona or maybe a return engagement to Greece, back by popular demand.

The Montana TV broadcast day starts off at 5:20 with a program called *Country Day* and then there's *Farm News* at 5:25 and *Sunrise Semester* at 5:30 and then as I said earlier we have *Early Farm Watch* at 5:50, followed by poetry coming to Montana at 6 a.m.

Poetry will assume the form of a program called *Poets Talking* about which *TV Guide* says: "The subtle changes in a work's meaning that occur when it is translated."

This is just what Montana needs and will be greeted by a large enthusiastic audience. I can see thousands of ranchers with their eyes glued to the set at 6 a.m., meeting and finding out about poetry and then spending the rest of the day talking about it with their neighbors.

"What do you think about poetry and that translation business and those lost meanings?"

"Well, I lost a calf last week and my first wife ran off with my best friend on my birthday. I never want to be twenty-seven again, so I listened with a kind ear and I sure hope they find those meanings. I miss the calf. The wife I don't. My second wife can cook. She isn't much to look at, but she can cook and she ain't going to run off with anybody."

Sunday

Standing in line at the checkout stand, the middle-aged man in front of me has his San Francisco Lord's Day all worked out. He unloads his basket, item by item, and puts his Sunday on the counter. First, there is a quart of cheap vodka, then a can of dog food, the newspaper and an artificial log for his fireplace.

The young male checker stares impassively on while this urban still life is assembled in front of him. He's seen enough of these customers not to care any more.

"Give me two packs of Marlboro 100's," the man says, finishing off his purchases. The man is a long way from a cattle ranch. I don't think he has ever smoked a cigarette in front of a herd of cows.

The checker rings it all up, and the man takes a very crisp ten-dollar bill out of his wallet. He folds it in half like a knife.

I'm forty-four years old.

Now: it's my turn.

Japanese Love Affair

I am watching a Japanese love affair from very close up. Actually, I am in bed with the lovers watching them fuck.

[243]

I am a part of their movement, but these are different lovers.

One of them is a film director and the other lover is film itself.

If you saw me right now, you'd just see somebody sitting quietly in a theater very carefully watching a movie, but I am not watching a movie, I am watching a passionate love affair in which each frame is a kiss, a caress, and each scene a lightning storm fuck.

Sometimes compared to the passion of art, human love affairs are studies in ice, like the skeleton of a refrigerator lying on its side near the North Pole.

Tap Dancing Chickadee Slaves

For John Fryer

There are not too many fables about man's misuse of sunflower seeds. Once upon a time there was an evil dance master who got the idea of using sunflower seeds to harness the energy of nature in a manner that would have met with Dr. Frankenstein's wholehearted approval.

The dance master was truly a very bad man because everybody knows that chickadees love sunflower seeds in the winter when heavy snows cover the ground.

Using sunflower seeds was a sure and diabolical way to enslave the hearts and minds of chickadees, and that's exactly what he did, buying twenty large birdfeeders and filling them up with sunflower seeds.

Soon hundreds of chickadees gathered at his place far out in the country and away from the prying eyes of men who possessed conscience or a desire to be President of the United States and use the issue of chickadee abuse as a beginning step to the Presidency.

The chickadees gorged themselves on sunflower seeds which he bought by the hundred-pound sack and soon the chickadees were totally in his power. They would do anything for those seeds.

. . . *anything.*

From that point on, it was only a short distance to teaching them to tap dance. Within a few months, he had a hundred tap dancing chickadees under his wing, so to speak.

He made little top hats for them and little canes to carry and he had them tap dancing on a huge ornate mirror lying on the kitchen table surrounded by dirty dishes and empty bottles.

He would put some good tap dancing music, Beethoven or Dixieland, on the phonograph and soon the birds would be tap dancing their little hearts out for more sunflower seeds.

[245]

Like a John Audubon Busby Berkeley, he taught them complicated precision routines that they would perform on that cursed mirror while he, their only audience, drank cheap gin out of a ten-year stale piece of hollowed out wedding cake.

Moral: Don't become too fond of sunflower seeds. Even if you're not a chickadee, you never know.

Pleasures of the Swamp

The pleasures of the swamp just keep happening to me, oozing down through my waking hours, alligatoring my perceptions of reality and teaching me that stagnant water has its own intelligence and can be as brilliant as a Nobel Prize winner if you deal with it on its own terms and don't try to make it into a Himalayan skyline.

Dangerous snakes?

I use them for silverware. They can turn a dull meal into an exciting experience. A hamburger steak can become a matter of life and death.

Mosquitoes?

They're just bloodthirsty flying air conditioners. After you lose your blood egotism, they are no problem.

Quicksand?

I think of quicksand as a telephone call to a lover. We have a nice conversation about secret weather and agree to meet next week at a coffee shop that resembles the pleasures of the swamp.

Sky Blue Pants

The Japanese girl doesn't know it but this is the greatest day of her life, the Mount Everest of her existence. She is maybe eighteen. I'll have to make a guess because I never saw her face. I don't know what will happen after today, but it will never get any better for her.

Getting off the Yamanote Line train at Harajuku Station, she is walking along in front of me with a young man beside her who possesses the clarity of a boyfriend.

She is wearing a pair of very light blue pants that cling

to her body like the sky fits the earth. The pants are not an accident. She has a magnificent body and walks like a Twentieth Century shrine in the pleasure of its own worship. She is totally aware of every movement and shadow her body casts. She can feel the power of her body's religion by watching prayers in the eyes of men.

At one point in the station, she reaches back and gives her own ass a cute little caress and it makes her happy. She knows a great thing and it's all hers. Lovingly touching it, she is very happy.

If she lives to be a hundred, life will never be the same again.

Kyoto, Montana

Southeast of Helena

In Kyoto, there is a Buddhist shrine called the Moss Garden where moss grows in a thousand colors and textures and each variation of the moss is a form of music, so pure in detail that it shines like a green light for the soul to go.

The Moss Garden is over six centuries old, so that's a lot of music and prayers rising like mist off the moss.

Here in Montana there is a small canyon that narrows to a rocky gorge filled with a grove of cottonwood tress. In the autumn, they look like a yellow waterfall seeming to come and go from nowhere.

A Different or
the Same Drummer

It's a very old story that takes place in every culture on this planet Earth: A kid with some drumsticks pounding on everything in sight. He cannot take his drums with him, so he changes everything around him into drums.

For weeks now I have watched a Japanese teenage boy and his drumsticks. I have seen him drum on trees, the backs of chairs, walls, tables, and parked bicycle seats.

A few moments ago the world within listening distance was filled with the sound of a hard drumming song pounding out of a pair of speakers in a café.

[249]

I turned and saw the boy drumming in perfect rhythm on the air and it was as if the sound of the drums was coming from his sticks.

When 3 Made Sense
for the First Time

A reasonable facsimile of a crime against nature attended a cocktail party in his mind. The facsimile was an interesting guest and provided entertainment for the other guests who when photographed together in a group portrait were his intelligence.

The facsimile of a crime against nature told some amusing anecdotes and then started to dance. The other guests watched with fascination. Then the telephone rang and it was for the facsimile who answered the phone and had to leave immediately because it had forgotten a previous engagement that was being held out in the country many miles away.

Apologies and farewells were made followed by departure. There was a brief shuffle of momentum and then the party continued. This time a memory of his childhood was the center of attention.

The memory dealt with the first time that he understood that the number 3 stood for 3 things like 3 apples.

A One-Frame Movie about a Man Living in the 1970s

Three years passed and nothing happened.

During the first year he didn't notice that nothing was happening. Halfway through the second year, it slowly began to dawn on him like the dawn that occurs in a rejected cartoon, a cartoon that nobody wants to publish in their magazine or newspaper, that finally ends up being thrown out by the cartoonist who eventually forgets that he ever drew it.

. . . with no copies of it left and no memory of it ever having been done . . .

That kind of dawn began to occur halfway through his second year of nothing happening.

By the time the third year was barely in progress he

realized fully that nothing was happening. Then he started to think about it.

He didn't know if it was a good thing or a bad thing.

That took another eleven months which brought him to the end of the third year of nothing happening. By that time he wondered if he really missed things happening or was he suffering from a simple case of nostalgia, another victim of the past.

He decided to wait one more year to see how he felt.

No reason to jump into anything, he thought. *You don't want to get into water over your head.*

My Tokyo Friend

Groucho:
Harpo and Chico said that after they died they'd send out a message if they could.

George Jessel:
Have you heard anything from them?

Groucho:
Not a goddamn word.

My friend here in Tokyo has been Groucho Marx in his eighties. I brought with me from America a 586-page book about Groucho as an old man and I've been reading it whenever I want to have some company.

The book is called *Hello, I Must Be Going* written by Charlotte Chandler who was a friend of his. She approaches Groucho from every angle. There are personal recollections of him plus conversations between him and people that he knew and liked: Woody Allen, George Jessel, Bill Cosby, Jack Nicholson, etc. There are also interviews with his living brothers Gummo and Zeppo.

Harpo and Chico are of course . . . not a goddamn word.

For six weeks I have had an old Groucho Marx for a friend. I am sorry that it has had to be a one-way friendship. I've read hundreds of anecdotes about him and laughed and been amazed by his wit and imagination.

When not spending time with him mirrored by the book high above Tokyo in my little hotel room, I think about him wherever I go. I'll be on a train staring out the window and instead of seeing Tokyo, I'll be looking at a photograph of Groucho Marx in his eighties.

It looks like Tokyo to everybody else but it's Groucho to me.

Halfway though dinner by myself Groucho will sit down beside me and say something funny and I will smile.

Or I'll be talking with some very serious Japanese intellectuals and Groucho will sneak up behind us as only Groucho can sneak up. And he will say something like, "Either this man is dead or my watch has stopped." I'll laugh and the Japanese people will wonder why I am laughing. They will look quizzically at me and I will apologize by saying, "Excuse me, I just thought about something funny." They will try to understand this American of uneven strangeness but they really won't be able to.

Having made me laugh Groucho silently leaves, disappears into the shadows of the room, the shadows that go on forever, taking you away into death.

Sayonara, Groucho.

Chicken Fable

I almost think of them as people. Yesterday it was windy here in Montana and they were Italians because I fed them some spaghetti. They did a comedy imitation of a banquet in Rome, celebrating some kind of obscure fraternal organization anniversary. The 81st anniversary of the death of the mother of the founding father of The Sons of Italian Eyeglass, Train and Bicycle Lovers.

As the chickens ate spaghetti for the very first time, their brown feathery bodies were wind-driven like grass and a part of the early morning sun patterns.

The chickens were all talking about the spaghetti.

Maybe that is why I think of them as sort of people, because they never stop talking. They always have something to say.

While seventeen chickens were dining in Rome, the eighteenth chicken was in the chicken house laying an egg. She had her head turned sideways toward the spaghetti benefactor. The wind glistened off one very bright eye, staring at me.

Today the chickens were Orientals because I fed them some leftover rice. They very carefully examined first bites of rice, using their beaks as chopsticks and soon were enjoying a good time in China.

Moral: It is difficult to go any place in this world without being close to the grave of a chicken.

The Fence

It is just another block-sized vacant lot filled with the oblivion of urban memories. There used to be houses there filled with people in disappeared-ago ages. The houses are gone and the people are gone. They all, more or less, wore out at the same time. Now the vacant lot waits for new houses and new people to fill them.

In another hundred years or so, it will be a vacant lot again.

The lot is guarded by a Cyclone fence as if anyone wanted to steal the emptiness held prisoner inside. The dry yellow grass of summer passing covers the lot which has rolling contours to it like small hills. I think a series of partially filled in basements have created the illusion of hills. It is the miniature of a larger landscape.

An old man with a cane stares intently or maybe it's only abstractly through the fence at the vacant lot. I wonder what he sees in there that demands so much of his remaining attention. Perhaps, he lived there when houses still bloomed. Somehow, for no reason at all, I doubt that, but often I'm wrong these days. I've been so wrong recently that because I don't think the old man lived there ensures the fact that he did.

Staring at the vacant lot causes him to almost miss his bus. I sit down next to him. I look at the back of his hands that hold the cane between the isolation of his thin, worn-out legs. His hands are covered with death freckles that are so thick they almost look like an aerial photograph of some Mayan ruins abandoned in the jungle.

The old man opens his mouth to yawn. He still has his own teeth. God, they're *old*. They look as if a slice of fresh white bread would be an almost insurmountable challenge.

Then I smile to myself.

[256]

They put a six-foot-high Cyclone fence around a vacant lot to keep this old man out. What did they think he was going to do? Climb over that fence and rebuild the past, put all the houses and the people back just the way they were?

Subscribers to the Sun

It's morning and soon the Teletype will start and this hotel in Tokyo will be connected like a bridge directly with the events of the world as they happen.

Now the teletype is still asleep, getting its last winks in before it's awakened to bring us what historians centuries from now will remember as July 17, 1978.

As the machine sleeps soundly here in the lobby of the Keio Plaza Hotel, history waits just a few moments away to be recorded by the machine which will be awakened by an alarm clock that instead of ringing, it will wake the machine up by printing the word TESTING followed by six apostrophes '''''' and then the letters:

M
MN
MNN

That is a different way to be awakened, followed by more letters and then the almost religious chant of the wire service machine:

THE QUICK BROWN FOX JUMPS OVER THE LAZY DOG.
THE QUICK BROWN FOX JUMPS OVER THE LAZY DOG.

The first test pattern ends with:

END HOW RCVD?"""""

The alarm continues to wake up the machine by typing out the first message five times for a total of ten wake-up foxes jumping over ten wake-up lazy dogs and five END HOW RCVD?"""""
Then the machine is totally awake, ready for the day and its first message comes out, connecting it with the third planet from the sun, Earth:

:ATTENTION SUBSCRIBERS:
GOOD MORNING